# The Evolution of a Successful Band Director

## workbook and study guide

A Proven Plan to Improve Your Effectiveness

# Scott Rush

AUTHOR OF

HABITS OF A SUCCESSFUL BAND DIRECTOR

GIA Publications, Inc.
Chicago

**The Evolution of a Successful Band Director**
**Workbook and Study Guide**
**A Proven Plan to Improve Your Effectiveness**
Scott Rush
www.habitsofsuccess.com

G-7440
ISBN: 978-1-57999-742-7
Copyright © 2009 GIA Publications, Inc.
7404 S. Mason Avenue, Chicago, IL 60638
www.giamusic.com

To Michelle,
whose habits of success change young lives each and every day.

# Table of Contents

# Foreword

If we are fortunate, each of us in this wonderful profession of music education will have been guided by a multitude of influences: inspirational teachers, life-changing repertoire, unforgettable performances, great friendships and, perhaps most importantly, our students—those very people to whom we have dedicated our lives to serve. One person who has taken the opportunity to reflect on this journey is Scott Rush, who shared with us his own insights in *Habits of a Successful Band Director*. That book has proven to be a most valuable resource for everyone who aspires to improve virtually everything about their teaching, whether interpersonal relationships, personal growth, efficiency of rehearsals, or a higher standard of music making.

In his new companion book, *The Evolution of a Successful Band Director*, Scott helps his audience achieve growth by evaluating their effectiveness and offering significant suggestions on how to improve upon it. This is not simply another "how to" book but rather an organized approach to assist readers in achieving those qualities of teaching to which we all aspire. The emphasis here is on self-evaluation and improvement, music making, professional issues and, most importantly, people issues.

We are indeed fortunate to have these two important books at our disposal. Scott Rush is a compelling writer, a master teacher, and a dedicated family man who has contributed significantly to the lives of his students—and now to his valued profession. As one who has had the privilege of working with his students, I can personally attest to the man, his methods, and the significant results those methods produce.

Thanks, Scott…for sharing your love of teaching, your commitment to excellence, and your insights on the journey each of us take.

—Rodney Winther
Cincinnati, Ohio

*Rodney Winther is Director of Wind Studies at Cincinnati College-Conservatory of Music. He has also made frequent appearances as a guest conductor and clinician across the U.S. and abroad.*

# Introduction

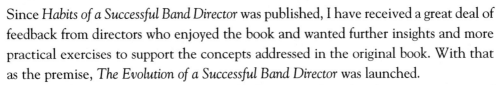

Since *Habits of a Successful Band Director* was published, I have received a great deal of feedback from directors who enjoyed the book and wanted further insights and more practical exercises to support the concepts addressed in the original book. With that as the premise, *The Evolution of a Successful Band Director* was launched.

Many leading authorities on leadership strongly subscribe to a process of continually evaluating one's effectiveness and trying to improve upon it. Believing that there is always room for improvement, I was motivated to expand on the work I had done with *Habits*. I chose to create *Evolutions* in a workbook format because I strongly believe that the process of noting your thoughts and feelings about your teaching situation on paper will be a huge growth experience for you and provide clarity about how you can improve. The workbook format uses probing questions, exercises, and key concepts to help you establish a written plan for success. In the end, the epiphanies you have about your program and the goals and solutions you develop are about helping your students along their journey towards becoming better musicians and people.

*The Evolution of a Successful Band Director* is divided into four sections:

Part I:      Teaching Strategies that Lead to Music Making
Part II:     Self-Evaluation
Part III:    Professional Responsibilities
Part IV:    People Issues

Each section stands alone and can be read in the order that meets your greatest need. For instance, if you're a veteran director, you may choose to do the self-evaluation at the beginning, whereas a college student or novice teacher may choose to work on the self-evaluation process upon completion of the book. This workbook is about you. When you've finished reading the book, it should be filled with handwritten notes in the margins, answers to the many questions contained throughout the book, and the first draft of your professional mission statement. You should also take time to list the concepts and material that impacted you most.

This book is intended as a resource for both practitioners as well as students. I realized that the information and insights I had to share could be beneficial to both experienced and inexperienced conductors, as evidenced by two e-mails I received that make reference to *Habits*. The reason I chose the two messages that follow is because each director was at a completely different place in his career path. Understanding the immediacy and necessity to improve is key to making this evaluative process work at any point in one's career.

> I want to thank you for writing your book…I am currently taking over for a well-established band program that has a history of excellence. The expectations couldn't be higher, and this is the first opportunity that I've had to lead a group of this size and reputation. I am beginning my fourth year of teaching, and thanks to your book, I feel more prepared to build on the success of the past and take the band to new heights. I am using your book daily (it stays open on my desk) and am very excited about it. I hope to establish an atmosphere of "music making" that will make a lifelong impact on my students.

Here is a letter written from a completely different perspective…

> I am a retired band director of 42 years and have recently finished reading your book. I was very successful as a marching band director and have received many honors and awards for my years of service. I am ashamed to admit, however, that after reading your book, I have come to the realization that although I was an efficient manager of people, I did not equip my students to become great musicians. I wish your book had been around 42 years ago.

I share this with you because it has a direct bearing on how you proceed through the remainder of this book. To paraphrase the great Bruno Walter, there are three stages in the *evolution* of a teacher/conductor:

- New teachers think they know everything.

- Teachers who have been teaching from five to ten years experience the feeling that they know nothing and become unsure of themselves.

- Veteran teachers say they don't know everything but continue to learn and grow through their experiences.

I hope that regardless of which stage you're in, you feel the need to improve and learn. Now is the time to be at your best, and proceeding through this book will enable you to grow and achieve a new level of understanding.

We have a *huge* responsibility to develop great musicians. (Note that I didn't say we have a responsibility to develop "professional" musicians.) If that were our measuring stick, we would have all failed miserably from the productivity perspective.

Although some of our students may go on to become professional players or teachers (a wonderful and rewarding aspect), we owe it to all of our students to develop a profound appreciation for music and a keen sense for the process of music making. We should develop each student to be the best musician and person he or she can be with the hope that all of our students will continue playing their instruments at the next level and beyond. The world needs people who understand and resonate with music. What better medium to use in developing great people—yes, we're in the people business.

Renewal time may be the most valuable time you spend in your professional life, and this book has been designed with you in mind. It's time to initiate a personal plan for professional success, and this book is the tool to help get you there. Managers can run a band program, but **conductors inspire great musicians to make beautiful music.**

# Thoughts About Reading This Book

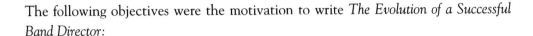

The following objectives were the motivation to write *The Evolution of a Successful Band Director:*

- Develop a companion document to *Habits of a Successful Band Director* that would present effective teaching principles with more depth and understanding.

- Devise a format that would encourage readers to apply and practice the principles and concepts as outlined.

- Challenge readers to look deep within themselves to find solutions that would lead to an effective teaching experience.

- Pose questions and suggest activities that would put these solutions into action and cause readers to set goals through self-discovery.

- Maintain the easy-to-read format of *Habits* and stay away from educational philosophy and psychobabble.

- Develop a more advanced book to address issues of the "seasoned professional," regardless of current track record.

- Make all of the principles outlined in the book applicable to any situation and not get stereotyped into a "cookie cutter" methodology.

- Develop a dialogue and language that ultimately establishes the classroom as a laboratory for making music.

- Establish a mind-set intent on developing a culture for your band program that has as its core message: **I want to develop great people.**

- Provide a study guide that could be used in college methods classes as a companion to *Habits of a Successful Band Director*.

# Chapter One

# Equipping the Musical Toolbox

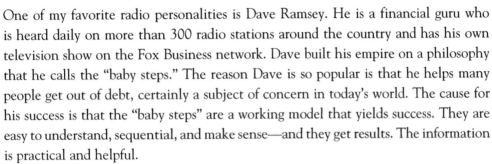

One of my favorite radio personalities is Dave Ramsey. He is a financial guru who is heard daily on more than 300 radio stations around the country and has his own television show on the Fox Business network. Dave built his empire on a philosophy that he calls the "baby steps." The reason Dave is so popular is that he helps many people get out of debt, certainly a subject of concern in today's world. The cause for his success is that the "baby steps" are a working model that yields success. They are easy to understand, sequential, and make sense—and they get results. The information is practical and helpful.

For many music educators, what is lacking is a model that yields success. If I ask you, "*What* do you want your students to be able to know, do, or sound like?" with some thought you could probably answer the question. The question might become a little harder to answer if I then ask, "*How* are you going to teach them to do those things?"

In the next several chapters, we are going to look at a model called **The Four Key Practices**. The model is an organizational framework that yields success. It's not a quick fix, nor does it excuse you from knowing your craft. The four key practices are deceptively easy, but hard to put into practice. They are exceedingly hard to do well, but with consistent practice can become acquired habits.

## Key Practice #1:
## Design a blueprint for what to teach.

Band directors have a *huge* responsibility, serving as the bridge from the beginning band student to the person deemed an artist. I was sitting at a Chicago Symphony Brass concert recently and heard every orchestra member who spoke say that their band directors and music teachers had a profound effect on their life. They went on to say that they didn't know what life would be like if they had never encountered these wonderful professionals and, consequently, music.

Determining *what* to teach is the initial step in the four key practices, and it is the beginning process of developing a great musician. One of the reasons I really like the model of the four key practices is that it works, regardless of the level of instruction. If you're a middle school director, this model will work. If your ensemble is more mature and you are responsible for teaching more advanced concepts, the model will yield success.

Key Practice #1 is based on the **Components of Playing**. Daniel Katzen, the former second horn player of the Boston Symphony, first introduced me to this concept. Here's the story:

> When I was in graduate school, part of my work-study program was serving as house manager for Jordan Hall, the incredible concert hall at New England Conservatory. I was approached by Daniel Katzen, second horn player in the Boston Symphony, about getting into the hall for an unscheduled rehearsal for his upcoming recital. He was performing a work for horn and harp, and the harpist could only practice late at night. I told him that the concert on Tuesday night ended around 10:15 and that if he wanted to start rehearsing around 10:30, it would be okay with me. I also asked if I could stay and listen. Following the rehearsal, he came up to me and said, "I really owe you one. How can I repay you?" Well, when you're in college, you have two immediate thoughts. The first is food or beverage, and the second is something a little more rational. I said, "What about a free lesson?" I had an audition coming up and really wanted someone to hear my excerpts. He agreed, and we arranged a lesson for sometime the following week. It was rumored at the time that Daniel Katzen's Boston Symphony audition was his forty-eighth audition, so if anyone knew about auditions and auditioning, he would be the one. I played my excerpts and was quite proud of my efforts. When I finished, I put my horn down (with the countenance of a trumpet player) and was waiting for him to pour out the accolades. Instead, he picked up a piece of paper and wrote on the top "Components of Playing." He wrote the number "1" and said, "What would you rate as the number one component of playing?" I said, "Tone," and he wrote down tone/sound. He then went to the bottom of the page and wrote the number "25." He said, "I am going to fill in the word "accuracy" as the least important thing, although it is important." (We are horn players, you know.) He then gave me two minutes or so to fill in numbers 2 through 24, encouraging me to be specific. After I quickly finished the list, he said, "This is what the committee is listening for in the audition—all of these things. To fully prepare for the audition, practice each one of these separately, and then perform your excerpts, concentrating on each component simultaneously."

There's the story! You are now going to be prompted to develop your own list. Stay focused on areas of individual musicianship right now. Don't include elements such as good posture or teaching key signatures on this list. There will be a place for that later in the book. Right now, focus on components of music making. You may include full ensemble musical concepts as well.

## The Components of Playing

1. _____

2. _____

3. _____

4. _____

*Practice each individually*

5. _____

6. _____

7. _____

8. _____

*Practice all simultaneously*

9. _____

10. _____

11. _____

12. _____

*Each requires some form of acting*

13. _____

14. _____

15. _____

16. _____

17. _____

The Components of Playing is nothing more than our list of *what* we should be teaching every day. I think we would all agree that each of the items on the list is something we are responsible for within the teaching process. What seemed at the time to be such a simple concept has proven to be the vehicle for much of the curriculum and the very thing that keeps us on track in trying to perfect every element of music. Mr. Katzen's method applies to band just as easily as it does to personal practice. We should often take a page from our personal practice sessions on our individual instruments and apply it directly to classroom instruction.

Here is an amended list from my original Components of Playing, which may help you fill in some of the blanks:

| | | |
|---|---|---|
| 1. | Tone | |
| 2. | Timing | |
| 3. | Tuning | |
| 4. | Dynamics | *Do each individually* |
| 5. | Phrasing | |
| 6. | Articulations (staccato, marcato, legato, slurred, various accents) | |
| 7. | Rhythm | |
| 8. | Balance | *Do all simultaneously* |
| 9. | Blend | |
| 10. | Attacks | |
| 11. | Releases | |
| 12. | Range | *Each requires some form of acting* |
| 13. | Endurance | |
| 14. | Musicianship (beauty, shape, interpretation, emotion, style, mood) | |
| 15. | Technique | |
| 16. | Tone color (intensity, color spectrum, sonority) | |
| 17. | Consistency / Accuracy (horn player mentality) | |

Practice each component individually and also simultaneously. This means that if you have an eight-measure passage that lacks musical integrity, you should start by trying to perfect each of the individual components necessary for its success (timing, phrasing, dynamics, articulations, etc.) and follow with a performance that tries to incorporate all of the components into one homogenous effort. This approach requires that the performer "act the part," whether from the standpoint of musical nuance, the composer's wishes, or some stylistic consideration. In other words, we don't want to simply be robots. We must become the music. There is an "acting" component to being a musician, and each individual work, if not every phrase, begs us to reveal the essence of the music.

# The Four T's

If you don't retain anything from this book, remember **The Four T's**. The Four T's are the anchors of the Components of Playing and are the building blocks for classroom instruction. They will invariably yield a fine-sounding ensemble.

## The Four T's are:

You must play…IN TIME,
　　　　　　　IN TUNE,
　　　　　　　WITH CHARACTERISTIC TONE,
　　　　　　　AND WITH APPROPRIATE TECHNIQUE

Several years ago, my nephew came to visit and brought along a friend. His friend was a high school trumpet player, and he knew I was a musician. To break the ice, we somehow got on the subject of practice. He asked me how much time I spent practicing. I answered his question and then after a long pause, I asked, "How much do you practice?" His response was, "I don't have to practice because I'm one of the better players in our band…the few times that I practice in a year is spent practicing my band music." This young man obviously didn't "get it," but I also wondered if he'd been taught how to practice. He could have started simply with The Four T's and developed a daily routine of practice.

If someone were to ask your students what they practiced, how they practiced, or how much they practiced, what would they say? If each of your students knew The Four T's, they could never claim there was nothing to practice.

# Teaching the Basics During Fundamentals Time

In the next two chapters, you'll be asked to develop a curriculum of teaching strategies for the various Components of Playing. In this section, let's look at what I believe to be the most important time of rehearsal: fundamentals time.

Fundamentals time (or warm-up time) is when we use effective teaching strategies to instill good, sound fundamentals of playing. Since Key Practice #1 is *what* to teach, let's ponder that with regards to fundamentals time.

Devise a list of the Components of Playing that should be specifically targeted during fundamentals time:

_____

_____

_____

_____

What fundamentals would you like to add to your warm-up that you are currently not teaching? Is there a component of playing you'd like to spend more time teaching?

_____

_____

_____

_____

Fundamentals time should be approached much like an individual practice session. If you think back to your college days, your private teacher probably had a prescribed warm-up routine for you to follow. This same approach should be utilized to develop each of the necessary fundamentals for playing a wind or percussion instrument. Full ensemble concepts such as balance and blend must also be addressed. Make a list of exercises you use during your personal warm-up routine that may be developed for band. You might also consider exercises your college applied professor asked you to incorporate into your daily routine.

_____

_____

_____

_____

_____

The following list is not intended to be definitive or sequential. However, it may prompt you to consider incorporating various exercises within your fundamentals time:

- Stretching
- Breathing exercises
- Mouthpiece buzzing
- Long tones
- Lip slurs
- Remington studies
- The whole-tone scale
- Attacks and releases
- Scale studies
- Low and high register
- Dynamics
- Chorales
- Balance
- Blend
- Timing
- Tuning
- Articulation
- Facility
- Clark studies
- Arpeggio studies
- Endurance exercises
- Phrasing and musicianship
- Sight-reading

A characteristic sound should be at the forefront of each of these studies and should be the overriding basis for fundamentals time. Answer the following questions and elaborate on your answers.

Is the purpose of the warm-up to get the chops in playing condition?

_____

_____

_____

_____

Is the warm-up time designed to teach balance, blend, tuning, attacks, releases, phrasing, articulations, etc.?

_____

_____

_____

_____

Is the warm-up routine for building strength?

_____

_____

_____

_____

# Chapter Checklist:

- Key Practice #1 is: Design a blueprint for what to teach.

- The Components of Playing is your list in response to Key Practice #1.

- The fundamentals time is when you teach it.

- The headliners of the Components of Playing are The Four T's:
timing, tuning, tone, and technique.

  As the song goes…

  Let's start at the very beginning,
  A very good place to start.
  When you read you begin with a, b, c,
  When you play an instrument—
      you begin with timing, tuning, tone, and technique.

  …Well, something like that.

# Chapter Two

## Planning and Implementing Effective Teaching Strategies

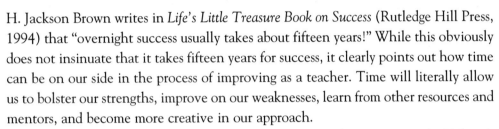

H. Jackson Brown writes in *Life's Little Treasure Book on Success* (Rutledge Hill Press, 1994) that "overnight success usually takes about fifteen years!" While this obviously does not insinuate that it takes fifteen years for success, it clearly points out how time can be on our side in the process of improving as a teacher. Time will literally allow us to bolster our strengths, improve on our weaknesses, learn from other resources and mentors, and become more creative in our approach.

Frances Hesselbein, former executive of Girl Scouts of America stated, "If there's anything I really believe in, it's the joy of learning and learning every day." I can honestly say that time and intense evaluative study has afforded me the ability to improve upon the strategies that I use to teach various concepts to my students, and these ideals have also allowed me to grow as an artist. Experience has also made me realize the importance of bringing in other artists to work with my ensemble, which is valuable for both my students and me. These have been treasured moments when I've been able to hone my skills (and steal really great ideas) by learning from other great musicians.

## Key Practice #2:
## Create effective strategies for how to teach the various components of playing.

If I started drilling you on *how* you teach each of the Components of Playing and stated that your success as a director was contingent on you answering each of the questions with an educationally sound methodology, it would be a challenging process. In this section, you should be able to articulate how you teach each of the various components, including the materials you use to aid in the teaching process. (Examples may include supplemental books, handouts, personally created study sheets, a personal method of teaching, or a myriad of technological tools now on the market.) You will be prompted to establish a teaching strategy for each Component of Playing and to seek multiple ways of teaching the same concept.

# Your Teaching Strategies for the Components of Playing

Write each Component, and then name a teaching strategy you utilize to teach the concept. Do not write, "I use the music that we are working on to…"

1. _____

_____

2. _____

_____

3. _____

_____

4. _____

_____

5. _____

_____

6. _____

_____

7. _____

_____

8. _____

_____

9. _____

_____

10. _____

_____

11. _____

_____

12. _____

_____

13. _____

_____

14. _____

_____

15. _____

_____

16. _____

_____

17. _____

_____

Answer the following questions as a follow-up to the strategies listed above:

What supplemental books do you use to aid in the teaching of the Components of Playing? Name the book, author, and component(s) it relates to. (Some supplemental books may help with more than one component.)

*Book*                    *Author*                    *Component*

_____

_____

_____

_____

What handouts do you give to your students as supplemental material for teaching the various Components of Playing? Title the handout and list the component(s) it relates to.

*Handout*                                          *Component*

_____

_____

_____

_____

What handouts have you personally created to help with the process of teaching the various Components of Playing?

_____

_____

_____

_____

What technology (computer programs, audio, etc.) do you use to help teach the various Components of Playing? Name the program or teaching aid.

_____

_____

_____

_____

## The Teaching Inventory Sheet

The **Teaching Inventory Sheet** (see page 17) is used to keep all of the above-mentioned information organized and to keep you focused and effective in your teaching. It is an organizational tool that keeps you on course and allows you to keep track of what's being taught. It is a quick blueprint of Key Practices #1 and #2, and is a basic list of *what* to teach and *how* to teach it (or a short list of the exercises you just completed). It is also the place to list issues that are non-musical but still very necessary for instruction. (Examples include proper posture, practice strategies, embouchure development, key signature recognition, enharmonic notes, transpositions, etc.) **Note:** This is what makes the Teaching Inventory Sheet different from the Components of Playing list, which is limited to applicable musical concepts.

The left column of the form—**Skill to Be Taught**—is the component. The right column—**Materials Needed /** *How* **to Teach It**—contains a list of the documents and strategies you use in tandem to teach a particular concept. (Example: If the component is **Rhythm**, the right side of the Teaching Inventory Sheet might say: **Use various rhythm sheets from** *Claude T. Smith's Symphonic Techniques* **and** *The Rhythm Bible* **by Dan Fox.**)

Use this organizational method for each of the various Components of Playing or other pedagogical strategies. Once this method is utilized for each component, divide the information on the Teaching Inventory Sheet into some type of sequence, which may include dividing the strategies into four nine-week segments. I use four Teaching Inventory Sheets over the course of a school year and decide when and how I want to teach each of the concepts. Some concepts are organized into a sequential model, while others are not. Concepts are prioritized based on the greatest need of the ensemble at the time. The information on the Teaching Inventory Sheet should be continually updated and adjusted based on newly acquired teaching techniques or information not covered during the previous nine weeks.

## Weekly Lesson Plans

Equally important to the Teaching Inventory Sheet is the **Weekly Lesson Plan**, which is pulled from the Teaching Inventory Sheet. Use the Weekly Lesson Plan to record very specific information and wording to help you monitor what is being taught in a given week. The Weekly Lesson Plan should be a reflection of the Teaching Inventory Sheet, and the two should allow you to see clearly what is being taught. As a Component of Playing (or musical concept) is taught, check it off of your Teaching Inventory Sheet. At the end of the nine weeks, all rows should be checked off. An example of a poor lesson plan is shown on page 18.

# Teaching Inventory Sheet

| Skill to Be Taught | Materials Needed / How to Teach It |
|---|---|
|  |  |
|  |  |
|  |  |
|  |  |
|  |  |
|  |  |
|  |  |
|  |  |
|  |  |
|  |  |
|  |  |
|  |  |
|  |  |
|  |  |
|  |  |
|  |  |

**Poor Sample Lesson Plan**

**Week of May 5–9**

| Monday, May 5 | Standard Addressed | Tuesday, May 6 | Standard Addressed |
|---|---|---|---|
| Announcements | | Announcements | |
| Warm-up | II, III, V | Warm-up | II, III, V |
| Chorale | II, V | Chorale | II, V |
| Solfege | I, V | Solfege | I, V |
| Music | II, V, VI, IX | Music | II, V, VI, IX |
| Assignment | | Assignment | |

The information is too vague and generic. It may meet a need for someone, but it doesn't serve as a blueprint for effective teaching. Instead, your lesson plan should directly correlate to your Teaching Inventory Sheet. A better template is shown on page 19.

This template is much more specific and can be expanded to include much more information. It addresses *what* was taught and is a snapshot of progress in action. There is nothing monumental or lofty about this template, but it is practical and it yields results.

## Lesson Plan Template

Week of _____          Ensemble _____

The following Components of Playing or concepts from the Teaching Inventory Sheet will be taught:

| *What* to Teach | *How* to Teach It |
|---|---|
|  |  |
|  |  |
|  |  |

The following fundamentals will be covered during warm-up time:

|  |
|---|
|  |
|  |
|  |

The following works will be programmed as part of the curriculum:

|  |
|---|
|  |
|  |
|  |

Concepts or notes to be covered as part of score study or assessment time (to include recorded material):

|  |
|---|
|  |
|  |
|  |

# Multiple Ways of Teaching the Same Concept

The easy part of teaching is presenting the material. Just about anyone can do that, and for some, that's where the teaching stops. The most difficult aspects of teaching are creating the desire to learn and the desire to master something. It's not enough to simply explain to students that you're going to spend the same amount of instructional time on class material whether they choose to learn it or not. It is our job to use our creativity to reach students and make *them* want to learn it.

In the previous section, you were asked to list a Component of Playing and name a strategy you use to teach it. What if that strategy simply didn't yield improvement or didn't work? Then what? In this section, you will be asked to name multiple ways of teaching a component. When considering each question, ask yourself: Do I have multiple ways of teaching this concept? Be creative!

1.  Name a thorough or sequential method for teaching the component of **Timing**:

    _____

    _____

    _____

2.  Name a thorough or sequential method for teaching the component of **Tuning**:

    _____

    _____

    _____

3.  Name a thorough or sequential method for teaching the component of **Centering Pitch**:

    _____

    _____

    _____

4. Name a thorough or sequential method for teaching the component of **Tone**:

_____

_____

_____

5. Name a thorough or sequential method for teaching the concept of **Key Signature Recognition**:

_____

_____

_____

6. Name a thorough or sequential method for teaching the component of **Blend**:

_____

_____

_____

7. Name a thorough or sequential method for teaching the component of **Technique**:

_____

_____

_____

8. Name a thorough or sequential method for teaching the component of **Balance:**

_____

_____

_____

9. Name a thorough or sequential method for teaching the component of **Dynamics:**

_____

_____

_____

## Chapter Checklist:

- Key Practice #2 is: Create effective strategies for how to teach the various components of playing.

- You were asked to define your methodology and were given an organizational framework with the Teaching Inventory Sheet. The Teaching Inventory Sheet functions as the compass that keeps you on course with *what* you are teaching and *how* you are teaching it. It serves as the master document from which to glean both your weekly and daily lesson plans.

- You were also asked to come up with multiple ways to teach the same concept.

If you found this process frustrating, Chapter Three will definitely help fill in the gaps.

# Chapter Three

# Teaching the Various Components of Playing

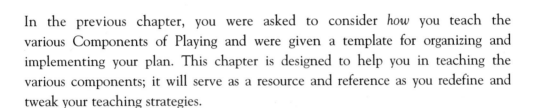

In the previous chapter, you were asked to consider *how* you teach the various Components of Playing and were given a template for organizing and implementing your plan. This chapter is designed to help you in teaching the various components; it will serve as a resource and reference as you redefine and tweak your teaching strategies.

## Timing

Timing involves both issues of steady tempo (playing in time) and rhythm within time (fitting rhythms into the time continuum). Wouldn't it be fantastic if our students came to us as already programmed machines that never made timing mistakes? The reality is that even the best musicians have to work at this skill.

Joe Alessi, principal trombonist of the New York Philharmonic, presented a workshop several years ago where he played several orchestral excerpts on audiotape for the audience. He explained that the recorded examples were audition tapes for acceptance into the Juilliard School. He played the first excerpt and asked the audience for feedback on the component of timing. The room of musicians (including myself) thought the timing was pretty solid. Mr. Alessi then explained that he was using a variable speed tape deck and said, "Can we all agree that if the timing is correct at the indicated tempo that it should also be perfect at a slower speed?" We all indicated that this was indeed true. Mr. Alessi then slowed the speed considerably. Upon listening again, it was obvious there were significant timing problems in several places. In a nutshell, this is a prime example of the degree to which we should insist on timing as a precise component. Much like tuning, timing is an exact science—this ain't horseshoes! I'm not advocating metronomic interpretations of music. However, students must be able to play precisely in time before the music can start to breath, ebb and flow.

The best tools I've seen to address timing issues include a metronome, some type of rhythm sheet (or rhythmic vocabulary), and the kinesthetic use of the body. Many directors have success with some form of clapping, foot tapping, and saying either the subdivisions of the beat or the rhythm itself. Here are some other strategies for addressing timing issues:

- Use a metronome and give a count-off of beat 1 only. Have the students audiate (hear) internally beats 2 and 3 and 4, and come in on the next downbeat. This establishes the need to subdivide at all times.

- Have students play the subdivisions of the beat using the pitches of the note itself. An easy example would be the rhythm of a dotted-eighth, sixteenth. Students should play the sixteenth subdivisions of the dotted-eighth (three sixteenth notes) aloud, followed by the written sixteenth, to demonstrate their understanding of subdivision. This concept can be applied to full phrases of music as well.

- Use a metronome and divide the tempo marking in half or, if possible, even further. (For example, for a work written in four, provide two beats per bar with the metronome. Follow that by providing only one beat per bar with the metronome.) Students are to internalize and audiate all missing beats. The natural tendency in this process is for students to rush.

- Ask students to play the attack but not the sustain of the note. (Some refer to this as "bopping"). This forces students to feel the inner beats and is great for ensuring that attacks are together and that notes line up. Another telling part of bopping is the tone quality on the attack. Many students will find that they don't work hard enough to produce a good sound when playing short notes.

- Have two students stand with their backs facing each other (like the beginning of a duel in an old western movie). Separate them by about five or six feet. Tell them you are going to give them a count-off of four beats (quarter note between 54–60). Explain that they are to keep time to themselves and when they reach count 32 to raise their right hand. Tell the rest of the class to watch the exercise and remain quiet until both students have raised their hands. This provides visual reinforcement that we don't inherently keep time.

- Ask students to figure exactly how many beats they are allotted in a piece of music. Most students don't realize that a metronome marking, a time signature, and the total number of measures can provide exactly what moment in time (on the time continuum) a piece should end. Give students a short example of eight measures, turn the metronome on (then off), provide the downbeat, and have them indicate when the piece should end. For example, an eight-measure piece of music at quarter note = 60, with a time signature of 4/4 would have its final release exactly 33 seconds from the time the piece started (not withstanding any ritardandos or rubato markings).

## Tuning

You're either in tune or out of tune. There is no gray area here. Once an ensemble reaches a certain level of maturity, 90% of the required listening skills should be spent devoted to tuning. I am convinced that tuning is what separates world-class ensembles from average ensembles.

It is difficult to play in tune because it requires focused listening, a working knowledge of basic tuning and instrument tendencies, and a myriad of other considerations. Our job is to teach our students what they need to know to be able to play in tune.

Write down issues that must be taught regarding the component of **tuning**. Don't worry about sequence at this point; throw caution to the wind and simply start writing.

_____

_____

_____

_____

_____

_____

When teaching the component of tuning, it is hard to know where to begin. You could start with individual instruments and work for days on various tuning pitfalls inherent to that one instrument. For instance, if we were discussing flute intonation, there are several teaching strategies you could use to discuss good intonation and adjusting pitch. Let me address one issue that seems to be a source of constant discussion among educators. The concept of flutes rolling in or out is somewhat of a misnomer. To produce a sound on the flute, one should blow to the back side of the tone hole where the air column splits, some going over the top of the tone hole and some going into the flute. (I find that most young players need to direct more air down into the instrument.) There is a spot where the best sound is achieved and the pitch is centered. A quick way to check this is to have students play on the head joint, which produces a Concert A. As the teacher, you should be listening to the best quality of sound and a centered pitch (if it's slightly flat, no worries). When adjusting pitch, if your students start messing with this *centered* sound by rolling in or out to a place that is less pleasing in tone, this is not a good adjustment. Some prefer the terminology "moving the lower lip in or out" or "jutting the jaw in or out" as a more appropriate way to teach this concept. However, a discussion with your players about not leaving the center of the sound while adjusting may be the most appropriate way to address this issue.

In addition, you should consider inherent bad notes or tendencies on the flute. For instance, third space C and C# along with these notes an octave higher (above the staff) are inherently sharp. The low register of the flute from low C to F is inherently flat, and the high register of the flute from high D#/Eb on up is inherently sharp. Students must also check the end plug to make sure it is adjusted properly.

This information just scratches the surface, and we've only covered one instrument. Each concert band instrument has similar pitfalls, and it's our job to teach our students how to play in tune. The following **tuning sequence** is not intended to be a thorough explanation of all tuning concepts, but it does describe issues we must address with our students. If you're a middle school director, you may choose to only incorporate the most necessary of these concepts as part of your curriculum, whereas a high school director should cover all of them.

**Tuning Sequence:**

1. **Tune with the tuner** (no audible pitch; visual process).
2. **Stop the needle on a stationary pitch** (requires a steady air stream).

Steps 1 and 2 are the only steps that are strictly visual in nature.

3. **Eliminate waves** (use your ears and try to achieve "beatless" tuning).
4. **Know how to adjust the instrument** (mechanics; tuning plug on flute).

This step may include knowing that an oboe reed should crow a "C" or sound a "B," and that only slight adjustments are possible with double reeds; knowledge of bocal size; etc.

5. **Learn inherent "bad" notes on the instrument** (pitch tendencies).
6. **Learn adjustments for "just" intonation** (major and minor chords).

Other adjustments would include bending pitch, humoring, finger shading, etc.

7. **Complete a pitch tendency chart** (good reference for your instrument).
8. **Play "in tone"** (many pitch problems will correct themselves).

**Other ways to improve intonation:**
- Good posture and breathing
- Sing and internalize parts
- Balance and blend within the ensemble
- Good embouchure development
- Play on good equipment, especially mouthpieces
- Have a working knowledge of how dynamics and temperature affect pitch

One of the best ways to begin the teaching process for tuning is to address **"beatless" tuning.** As students begin to hear this concept, they will learn that beats slow down and eventually go away when they bring the note into tune. Demonstrate this by having two students adjust their instruments in opposite directions. Have them play these adjusted unison pitches for the class. The initial unison note will be quite horrific! As the adjustment process takes place, students will hear the beats begin to slow down and then disappear. In teaching this component, you should also teach your students the following concepts:

Flutes....................... If you are sharp, roll in or lower the head slightly; if you are flat, roll out or lift the head slightly. Then adjust the instrument.

Brasses ........................ Match pitch by lipping up or down to eliminate beats, then adjust the instrument accordingly: if sharp, pull out; if flat, push in. Horns may use the right hand to make subtle pitch adjustments, especially in the low register. Trombones have a tuning slide in their right hand.

Bassoons ..................... You must have the proper bocal size as a starting point for pitch: if sharp, use a longer bocal; if flat, use a shorter size. The lower the number, the shorter the bocal, and vice versa.

Other woodwinds ...... This may be a departure from the norm, but I believe no embouchure adjustment should be taught to beginners—only adjust the instrument: if flat, push in; if sharp, pull out. As the director, you should check the proper adjustment of oboe reeds and the length of barrels for clarinet. I don't like to teach embouchure adjustment because I want the young players to concentrate on proper embouchure development, period! As they get a little older and start to experience the concepts covered on the pages that follow, then they are ready to learn other ways to adjust.

**Chordal Tuning:**

With regard to **"just"** **intonation,** here is a quick reference guide for adjusting chord tones:

When tuning major chords:

| | |
|---|---|
| **Root** | must be in tune |
| **Major 3rd** | must be lowered 14 cents |
| **Major 5th** | must be raised 2 cents |

When tuning minor chords:

| | |
|---|---|
| **Minor 3rd** | must be raised 16 cents |

Other tendencies in major:

| | |
|---|---|
| **Major 2nd** | must be raised |
| **All leading tones (7ths)** | must be raised |
| **Dominant 7ths** | must be lowered 31 cents |

**Tuning Tendencies:**

With regard to tuning and pitch centering for the various wind instruments, also consider the following:

Flute:
- Some prefer to use the terminology "moving the lower lip in or out" or "jutting the jaw in or out" as an appropriate way to teach pitch adjustment.
- Third space C and C# and above the staff C and C# are inherently sharp. The low register of the flute from low C to F is inherently flat, and the high register from high D#/E♭ on up is inherently sharp.
- Playing on the head joint produces a Concert A.
- Check the end plug to make sure it is adjusted properly.
- Use Concert A as the desired tuning pitch.

Oboe:
- No tuning adjustment of the instrument is required. The reed should go all the way in; a properly adjusted reed is paramount to good intonation. You may raise pitch by applying slight pressure to the firmness of the embouchure, as well as slight pressure toward the bottom lip.
- Fourth line D to top line F# are inherently sharp. The bottom four notes on the oboe (B♭ to C#) tend to be inherently flat.
- Oboes should sound a Concert B if playing on the reed or sound a concert C if crowing.
- Use Concert A as the desired tuning pitch.

Clarinet:
- To properly adjust the instrument, tune using open G for the barrel and third space C for the middle joint.
- Alternate fingerings and finger shading are vitally important to tuning a clarinet. Throat tones are especially tricky to tune; several choice alternate fingerings for throat tones may be required.
- For centering purposes, clarinets should sound a Concert F# on the mouthpiece and barrel. If sharp, students are probably not using enough air or are biting. They need to drop the jaw and voice properly to achieve the Concert F#.

Bass Clarinet:
- To properly adjust the instrument, use middle C as the tuning note and adjust the neck.

- Throat tones are out of tune; choice alternate fingerings may be required.
- Bass clarinets should sound a Concert C# with the mouthpiece and neck as a checkpoint for centering.

Bassoon:

- To properly adjust the instrument, use Concert A as the tuning note and adjust the reed or the size of the bocal if the pitch is sharp or flat: the higher the bocal number, the longer the length and, therefore, the lower the pitch.
- As with oboe, pulling out is not a viable option.
- Fourth space G is a very sharp note on the bassoon. Most inherent pitch flaws are sharp in nature; there are many alternate fingerings available to help with this.
- Bassoons should sound a Concert C on the reed and bocal for centered pitch.

Saxophone:

- To properly adjust the instrument, alto and bari saxes should tune to Concert A, and tenor saxes should tune to Concert F.
- Third-space C# is very flat; add the bottom side keys Bb and C. Fourth line D is very sharp; add the low B key. The extreme low and high registers are sharp on the saxophone. Try dropping the jaw a little and relax.
- The alto sax should sound a Concert Ab with the mouthpiece and neck. The bari and tenor saxes should sound a Concert E with the mouthpiece and neck.

Trumpet:

- To properly adjust the instrument, trumpets should tune to Concert F (written second-line G). Several times a week, trumpets should also approach Concert Bb by playing the notes (written) G, A, B, C (on Bb trumpet). The reason for this method is that many young players force on third-space C as a tuning note and learn to pinch the note sharp from the beginning of development. By using Concert F (written G) as the tuning pitch, a relaxed sound can be achieved. It is very important that players check the Concert Bb, however, because they may begin to pull the tuning slide out too far and play flat in the upper register.
- Each of the valve slides should be tuned in conjunction with the main tuning slide and each of the individual valve fingerings should be adjusted from the open tuning note.
- If trumpet players have the tuning slide out more than just over an inch, it is out too far (at room temperature). If this happens, students should push the slide in to the above-mentioned length and bring the pitch down using their hearing, embouchure, and oral cavity.

- Low D, C# and G, F# are inherently sharp; the third valve slide ring should be used to correct these pitches. Fourth-line D and fourth-space E and E♭ are inherently flat and should be adjusted. One means of adjustment is to use alternate fingerings of E (12), E♭ (23), and D (13). The (12) combinations of E and A in the staff are inherently sharp and can be corrected by using the third valve only or the first valve slide trigger.

Horn:

- To properly adjust the instrument, horns should tune to Concert C (written second-line G). The reason is that many young students force on third-space C and learn to pinch the note sharp. In addition, the third-space C is inherently sharp with the trigger, especially on instruments that have a separate B♭ tuning slide. This B♭ tuning slide is the first place to check if third-space C is sharp.
- Each of the valve slides should be tuned in conjunction with the main tuning slide, and each of the individual valve fingerings should be adjusted from the open tuning note. The F (no trigger—front) slides should be adjusted from the open G, and the B♭ (trigger—back) slides should be adjusted from third-space C. When tuning the B♭ side, make sure the B♭ tuning slide is adjusted properly for third-space C before continuing the tuning process with each of the valve slides.
- The B♭ (trigger) and F (no trigger) sides of the horn should be in tune with each other. The simplest way to check this is to play third-space C on the F side (no trigger) and make sure it's in tune. Then play it again on the F side and engage the trigger (B♭ side). The two notes should sound the same as you go back and forth. If the B♭ side is sharp, adjust the B♭ tuning slide (some horns have this, while others do not).
- Third-space C# is inherently sharp, and first-line E natural is typically flat. The (12 with trigger) combinations of A and D on the staff are inherently sharp and can be corrected by using the third valve with the trigger. I prefer teaching all beginners to use third valve for A and D because it develops their third finger and allows them to hear these notes closer to pitch. Once students are more experienced, third valve and the (12) combination should be used interchangeably as the pitch dictates.
- The right hand should be flat and open in the bell. It should go as far in as possible (and comfortable) and should remain open for normal playing. The right hand can be used as a means of correcting sharpness by closing the hand slightly in the bell. This is typically done in the low register but can be used for other notes that are inherently sharp.

Trombone:

- To properly adjust the instrument, trombones should tune to fourth-line F Concert (although a bit sharp). Several times a week, trombones should also approach Concert B♭ by playing the notes F, G, A, B♭. The reason for this method is that many young players force on the B♭ at the top of the staff and learn to pinch the note sharp. By using Concert F as the tuning pitch, a relaxed sound can be achieved. It is very important that players check the Concert B♭, however.
- If an instrument has an F attachment, play fourth-line F in first position on the open horn, and then engage the F attachment. If the F attachment is out of tune, adjust the F attachment tuning slide.
- Fifth partial D, D♭, and C above the staff are inherently flat. One means of adjustment is to use alternate slide positions D (flat 4), D♭ (flat 5), and C (flat 6). You can't raise the D in first position, so fourth position is the appropriate alternative.
- Trombone players have a tuning slide in their right hand; they must have a great sense of pitch to be able to master the instrument.

Euphonium (bass clef):

- To properly adjust the instrument, euphoniums should tune to Concert F. Several times a week, euphoniums should also approach Concert B♭ by playing the notes F, G, A, B♭. The reason for this method is that many young players force on the B♭ at the top of the staff as a tuning note and learn to pinch the note sharp from the beginning of development. By using Concert F as the tuning pitch, a relaxed sound can be achieved. It is very important to check the Concert B♭, however, because students may begin to pull the tuning slide out too far and play flat in the upper register.
- Each of the valve slides should be tuned in conjunction with the main tuning slide, and each of the individual valve fingerings should be adjusted from the open tuning note.
- If euphonium players have the tuning slide out more than two inches, it is out too far (at room temperature). If this happens, students should push the slide in to the above-mentioned length and bring the pitch down using their hearing, embouchure, and oral cavity.
- Low C, B and F, E are inherently sharp; the fourth valve should be used to correct these pitches. Top of the staff C, C#/D♭, and D are inherently flat and should be adjusted. One means of adjustment is to use alternate fingerings of D (12), D♭ (23), and C (13). The (12) combinations of D and G in the staff are inherently sharp and can be corrected by using third valve only.

Tuba:

- To properly adjust the instrument, tubas should tune to Concert F. Several times a week, tubas should also approach Concert B♭ by playing the notes F, G, A, B♭. By using Concert F as the tuning pitch, a relaxed sound can be achieved. It is very important that players check the Concert B♭, however, because they may begin to pull the tuning slide out too far and play flat in the upper register.

- Each of the valve slides should be tuned in conjunction with the main tuning slide and each of the individual valve fingerings should be adjusted from the open tuning note.

- Low C, B and F, E are inherently sharp; the fourth valve should be used to correct these pitches. Second space C and C# and third line D♭ and D are inherently flat and should be adjusted. One means of adjustment is to use alternate fingerings of D (12), D♭ (23), and C (13) in that register. The (12) combinations of bottom ledger-line D and first-line G in the staff are inherently sharp and can be corrected by using third valve only.

## Pitch Centering

Centering pitch is nothing more than playing a note in the middle or core of the desired pitch. Executing centered pitches creates resonance to the sound and produces the greatest number of overtones for a note, which causes the "ring" and core to the sound.

It is important to check young brass players on their mouthpieces because it is acoustically and physically possible to play a note on the instrument while simultaneously buzzing slightly above or below the pitch on the mouthpiece. A great exercise for brass players is to have them buzz simple children's songs on their mouthpiece. This will help internalize pitch, is great ear training, and will stress the importance of hitting notes in their center. Examples of these type songs include:

| | |
|---|---|
| Mary Had A Little Lamb | Twinkle, Twinkle Little Star |
| Hot Cross Buns | Silent Night |
| Three Blind Mice | Row, Row, Row Your Boat |
| Joy to the World | My Country 'Tis of Thee |
| Pop Goes the Weasel | Amazing Grace |
| Frosty the Snowman | Jingle Bells |
| Old McDonald Had a Farm | Rock-a-Bye Baby |

For woodwinds, the best pitch centering method is to use the pitch indicators listed previously (example: clarinet sounds a concert F# on the mouthpiece and barrel). The best centering exercises use a multi-note sequence (sounded through an electronic keyboard), which can be imitated and matched. On the Japanese DVD, *Basic Training for Concert Band* (distributed in the U.S. by Shattinger Music), a pitch sequence is used with concert B♭ as tonic. It is important to note that Yamaha makes a keyboard that can be set to "just" intonation. This method is demonstrated on the DVD with students from the Saitama Sakae High School Wind Orchestra.

**Evolutions Extra:** As an added bonus, use the children's tunes listed on the previous page as melodic identification for your students. Have them play the selections by ear on their instruments. This exercise can be used at the beginning of class. In addition, these are great to use as breathing exercises with breathing tubes.

A final word about tuning: **Never use tuners on everyone's stand as a means of addressing intonation problems!** There are a gazillion reasons why you should not use this teaching technique, but here are two: First, it doesn't account for "just" intonation at all (see "Chordal Tuning" on page 28). Second, tuning is a listening process, not a visual one. Our job is to train students' ears, not their eyes. The only logical use for a tuner is to tune during individual practice sessions or to help establish an ensemble tuning pitch.

## Tone

For teaching and developing a mature sound, it is imperative that students have good examples or models to listen to, such as a private teacher, a recording, or a master class experience. We asked one of the military band euphonium players to present a master class for our low brass students. After the master class, one of our ninth grade euphonium players came to me and said, "I didn't know that's what a euphonium was supposed to sound like." After that experience, I told all of our euphonium players that as they took their first breath, they should say to themselves, "I am Don Palmire." They would then try to imitate Don's sound.

Another effective teaching tool for good tone is to make recordings available to students in the form of a listening library. Have two or three great players on each of the instruments represented in your library and share them with your students. Have students evaluate and assess what they hear in these recordings. Here are examples of great artists to consider for your listening library:

Flute .................... Jean-Pierre Rampal, Jim Walker
Clarinet ................. Harold Wright, Larry Combs, Jon Manasse
Oboe ..................... Joseph Robinson, John Mack
Bassoon ................. Bubonic Bassoon Quartet, Christopher Millard
Saxophone ............. Eugene Rousseau, Joseph Lulloff, Steven Mauk

Trumpet.................Phil Smith, Chris Martin, Tim Morrison
Horn ......................Dale Clevenger, Dennis Brain
Trombone..............Joseph Alessi, Christian Lindberg
Euphonium............Brian Bowman, Roger Behrend
Tuba......................Arnold Jacobs, Sam Pilafian
Mallets..................Dave Samuels, Gary Burton, Evelyn Glennie

Another important teaching trait is to have basic troubleshooting/knowledge skills in the area of tone production. Your teaching toolbox should contain appropriate verbal skills in teaching tone production on each of the instruments. For example, you may make the following comments when working with the clarinets on tone production:

Clarinet:

- Firm corners, flat chin—pull your chin down like a frown.
- Pressure up towards the top teeth with your thumbs—don't bite.
- Drop the jaw and play with an open throat. An open throat doesn't refer to an oral cavity formation or tongue placement; the oral cavity formation for clarinet is *not* an "oh" syllable but is shaped much like a hiss (see below for articulation).
- You should have enough mouthpiece in your mouth so you are just short of the "squeak point."
- When articulating, the tongue should be light as a feather touching the reed, but there must be plenty of air behind the tongue. Strive for a clear sound, not a reedy or subtonish sound.
- Try using a "lee" articulation or the French sound "leur," with the tip of the tongue on the tip of the reed. Keep it light.

These examples represent the type of working knowledge you must have on each of the instruments. I have found the best resources to be college professors, who are more than willing to give advice on good tone production.

# Blend

Blend is the combining of two or more tone qualities. Sometimes they are tone qualities of like instruments and other times they are combinations of various instruments or instrument groupings. Early in my teaching career, someone asked me, "How do you teach blend to your students?" At the time, I really didn't have an answer. I could explain the concept of blend, but I couldn't recite my arsenal of how I taught it. Here are some analogies for teaching blend:

- The three-person rule
- Getting sounds inside other sounds to match timbre (listen up the section)
- Name ways to stick out of the ensemble
- Ensemble sound: chocolate cake story
- Blending of two instruments (clarihorn or hornet)

- **The three-person rule**
  Ask students to create trios around the ensemble by listening to the people on their left and right. When instructing them to listen, make sure you explain that they are to paint their sound into the sound of their neighbor and try to match the best tone quality in the section.

- **Getting sounds inside other sounds to match timbre**
  In an ideal world, all players should listen up the section and match the sound of the principal player, as well as get their sound inside the sound of the person who sits above them. This does not take into account situations of balance, when lower parts may need to be louder than upper parts. When explaining this analogy, point out that if tuning is incorrect, it will be difficult to blend sound.

- **Name ways to stick out of the ensemble**
  One of the best and simplest questions to ask a young ensemble is, "In what ways can one stick out of the ensemble?" The list will certainly include playing too loud, playing out of tune, playing out of tone, etc. This exercise can establish an elementary dialogue about matching sounds. You can also use the students' list to show that they know what to listen for within the ensemble. Then hold them accountable to their self-created list.

- **Ensemble sound: chocolate cake story**
  My friend, Gary Gribble, finally admitted that he stole this analogy from Paula Crider. Begin the chocolate cake story by telling the students that you're going to serve them chocolate cake. Walk out with an imaginary cake plate and open it to reveal not a chocolate cake, but each of the individual ingredients of a chocolate cake. Ask a flute player in the front row to open her mouth and you'll gladly start throwing in eggs, flour, sugar, chocolate, and all the other ingredients of your chocolate cake. Then ask, "Did that taste like a wonderful slice of chocolate cake?" The obvious answer yields that it is the blending of each of the ingredients that makes a cake taste wonderful. Likewise, it is the blending of the individual sounds within the wind band that makes a wonderful, sonorous sound.

- **Blending of two instruments (clarihorn or hornet)**
  It is important for students to understand that blending two different timbres within the ensemble is a rare skill. Yet when it's right, it sounds incredible. There is a wonderful moment near the end of John Gibson's *Resting in the Peace of His Hands* where the principal trumpet and alto sax play in unison. As the conductor, you can certainly decide to defer to the trumpet sound or the sax color, but a true blended sound would create neither. It would create a new, unique color one could call "trumpax" or "altet." (The example used in the title would illustrate clarinet and horn.) Regardless of the combination, when performed with care, creating these new colors is a wonderful experience for listeners.

## Balance

When we hear the word "balance," most of us think of the McBeth pyramid system of balance. This system is based on the premise that the bass voice should be predominant in the sound, and the overall sound should be built from the bottom up. Francis McBeth illustrates this concept as follows:

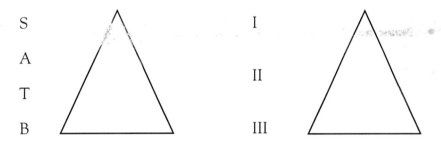

In this example, the double-pyramid approach refers to both the SATB model (more bottom than top) and the balance within parts. In this case, one would ask for more sound from the thirds and build the sound within the section from the bottom up. Thus, when distributing parts it is important to put more players on the lower parts from the outset. However, contemporary orchestration and instrumentation dictate that we make careful decisions about balance.

In addition to this type of balance, some of the same skills necessary for good blend are also put into practice for balance, including:

- Getting sounds inside other sounds to match timbre (listen up the section)
- The three-person rule

In each case, players should be asked to listen down to the lowest voice in their family (woodwinds down to bass clarinet and brasses down to tuba) and then listen to the next lowest instrument in the SATB choir to make sure they are not playing louder than the desired balance intends. High voices should get their sounds inside the sounds of lower-voiced instruments and let the band sound be molded from the bottom. Some directors prefer to balance the entire band to the tuba section, and I am aware of a few who balance the entire ensemble down to the bass clarinets. A word of caution: Make sure the brass section does not dominate the overall band sound.

The three-person rule should be put into practice when the upper register (especially with the soprano voices of flute, clarinet, and trumpet) becomes too bright and thin or when the upper voices stand out in general. This is common with younger ensembles. We have three concert bands, and the second and third bands definitely have issues with lack of maturity and control in the upper register. As such, this becomes a balance and blend issue. It's especially noticeable in obbligato woodwind parts within marches.

When teaching the concept of balance to young students, one really effective way to demonstrate the point is to have them play the pyramid concept upside down or inverted, demonstrating incorrect balance. Have the high voices really give it a hearty rip, and bring the bass voices down to a murmur. Young people actually like doing this because it sounds so bad! After making sure students understand the wrong way to achieve proper balance, then have them play it correctly. This can also be demonstrated to parents at a concert, especially at the middle school level.

Now, here's my disclaimer about balance: One balance concept does not fit all, so be careful. Different composers and many contemporary works require different types of balance, so don't use this model for everything you play. For example, never cover the melody. Musical texture with regards to priority of parts is central to good balance. Another example would be the music of Persichetti; he typically writes in choirs of instruments, and where pyramid balance works within the choirs, the word "clarity" is much more important in his music. If you simply strive for alternating choirs of sound, you've pretty much missed the point of his music. I think of balance as having *two* distinct aspects: (1) balance in terms of color (treble vs. bass instruments) and (2) balance in terms of texture (melody vs. accompaniment).

Another really important concept of balance is the natural tendency for wind instruments to drift sharp or flat during dynamic changes. Single reeds typically go flat during a crescendo and sharp during a diminuendo, whereas flutes and all brasses typically go sharp during a crescendo and flat while getting softer. (I leave double reeds out of this equation completely because they usually bend pitch so much that it's a crapshoot.) Because of this natural tendency to drift away from the pitch center, the appropriate instruction during dynamic changes would be for the musicians to be aware of both their percentages and tendencies. The percentages refer to the place where each instrument lies within the SATB pyramid. You may ask soprano voices to only crescendo 40%, while tenor voices are using 80% and bass voices 100%. When executing a dynamic change, students must keep the pitch centered and aurally cling to the initial pitch.

There is a great deal of work necessary to execute a perfect ensemble crescendo or diminuendo, especially if it's a major chord.

### Balance

**Pyramid balance**
**Melody versus accompaniment / overall texture**
**Woodwinds balance down to bass clarinets**
**Brasses balance down to tubas**
**Balance during dynamic changes**

| | |
|---|---|
| Bass voices | 100% |
| Tenor voices | 80% |
| Alto voices | 60% |
| Soprano voices | 40% |

**Clarity disclaimer:**
**One balance concept does not fit all!**

# Dynamics

Okay…I'll admit it. I don't insist that my ensembles play with a large enough dynamic spectrum. Dynamics are generally a weak point within our ensembles, and most of the time, the problem can be traced back to me because I don't say, "You can play that softer." One of our exercises during fundamentals time is devoted to dynamics, so it's not that we don't focus on it. It is simply a matter of my students developing the control and me insisting that they do it. The component that makes performing and listening to a performance so exciting is dynamics because it provides the color palette. The *mezzo* dynamic is the equivalent of black and white. If we want bright red or fuchsia, then we must get outside of our small dynamic box and take a chance.

World-class ensembles have the ability to push the envelope in both directions. I remember a particular performance of the Boston Symphony Orchestra playing the "Adagietto" movement from Mahler's Fifth Symphony. As they started the "strings" movement, I was immediately struck by how soft (*pianissimo*) and musically the orchestra was playing. The sound was both contemplative and haunting, and it clearly communicated an emotional intent. As the movement progressed, I found myself on a musical journey that came to a gushing arrival point of *fortissimo* when the celli and basses performed the descending arpeggio near the end of the movement. It was one of those moments when I wasn't sure where I was or what I was doing—I was transfixed in the moment. It is certainly a moment I'll never forget. After reflecting on the performance, I decided that the care taken at the beginning of the movement to truly play softly is what allowed everything else to work.

Answer these simple questions:

What exercises do you use to teach dynamics?

_____

_____

_____

_____

_____

What do you do when your students are not playing dynamics effectively?

_____

_____

_____

_____

_____

This seems like such a simple answer, but for me the honest answer would be that I sometimes ignore it. Here are a few examples of dynamic exercises that are particularly effective:

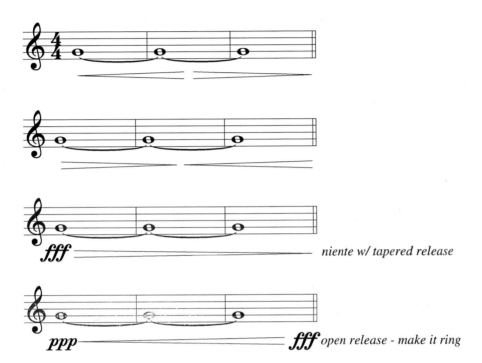

# Precision

One of the most basic ensemble concepts is playing together, yet it is sometimes the most overlooked and underprepared. We've all heard ensembles that fail to match articulations and that have poor attacks and releases. Timing also plays a role with precision, and each of these issues must be addressed.

The **five-step scale study** is effective in teaching articulations. Various tonguing and slurring articulations can be performed along with displaced accents. Here are some examples:

*When performing displaced accents, be aware of producing a good sound on the accented notes.*

The **attack pattern** is useful in dealing with initial attacks, as well as addressing the beginning, middle, and ends of notes. Many directors focus on good initial attacks but don't spend nearly enough time on duration and releases (especially tapered ones). The following attack pattern can be used to address each of these components. When performing this with a full ensemble, each instrument group should play their pitch. No transposing is required, so be prepared for the chord to feel a little strange at first. Once the students hear it, it is a great exercise in vertical listening.

*Using this pattern . . .*                    *Insert the following notes.*

Ultimately, precision is a direct result of students listening intently enough to make clear entrances (breathing together is paramount), match articulations, and play together. One effective technique in addressing precision issues is for the conductor to get off of the podium and stop conducting. Once you give the initial breath through the prep beat, just get off of the podium. Both you and your students can learn through this process, and it allows for a healthy discussion on precision.

## Key Signature Identification

One of the basic components we are responsible for teaching is key signature identification. There are always individual students within our program who haven't mastered key signatures.

Here are a few traditional (and not so traditional) strategies for teaching key signature recognition.

Start with the order of flats and sharps. When you ask students to tell you what sharps or flats are in the key signature, they most often tell you the order as they appear in the scale. It is vitally important that students always recite sharps or flats in their proper order.

**The order of FLATS:**     B E A D G C F
**The order of SHARPS:**   F C G D A E B

Here are the traditional rules for finding a particular key:

**FLATS:**    The next-to-last flat in the key signature *is* the key.

**SHARPS:** Go to the last sharp in the key signature, then go up one half-step. That *is* the name of the key.

**Circle of Fifths:**

## MAJOR KEYS

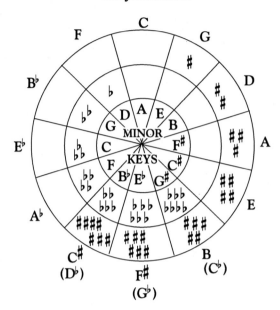

The **Circle of Fifths** (clockwise) or **Circle of Fourths** (counterclockwise) is also a great resource for teaching keys, both major and relative minor. By using this system, students are either adding sharps or taking away flats. This is reversed if using the Circle of Fourths.

In the Circle of Fifths, you add sharps as you go clockwise and subtract flats. This tells you how many sharps or flats are in each key. It does *not* tell you which sharps or flats, but you always follow the order of sharps and flats (previous page).

**McGrew's Fourths:**

Here is another clever way of presenting information for key recognition. It's a form of fourths that is very practical. Begin by writing the following sequence of notes:

C    F    B    E    A    D    G

You may teach these notes through any means, or you can displace two notes from the order of flats and place them at the beginning of the sequence.

Next explain a couple of truisms for this exercise. The first truth is that you are going to number from zero to seven, and then back to zero. The reason you are using the key numbers of zero through seven is to answer the following questions:

1. Why do we start with zero?   *Answer: The key of C has no sharps or flats.*
2. Why do we go to seven?      *Answer: There are only seven possible sharps or flats.*

Then explain that as you begin numbering from zero to seven, the top row represents the number of flats in the key signature for flat keys (except C, which has no sharps or flats), and the bottom row represents the number of sharps in the key signature for sharp keys. When demonstrating this method to students, make sure you insert the numbers in the following fashion:

|   | 0 | 1 | 2 | 3 | 4 | 5 | 6 | 7 | 6 | 5 | 4 | 3 | 2 | 1 |
|---|---|---|---|---|---|---|---|---|---|---|---|---|---|---|
|   |   |   |   |   | 0 | 1 | 2 | 3 | 4 | 5 | 6 |   |   |   |
| Flats (♭) |   |   |   |   | C | F | B | E | A | D | G |   |   |   |
| Sharps (#) |   |   |   |   | C | F | B | E | A | D | G |   |   |   |
|   |   |   |   |   | 7 | 6 | 5 | 4 | 3 | 2 | 1 |   |   |   |

The one flaw in this system is that it doesn't account for the key of C flat. Explain this when teaching the system. Many students who have difficulty with the traditional ways of learning key signature recognition automatically gravitate to this method and master the concept.

## How to Practice

We are all quick to chastise our students for not listening. We often say, "You're not listening," but do students really know what they should be listening for, or for that matter, what we're hearing? Instead we can say, "You're not listening for good balance, tuning, tone…"

Practice is the same way. We often make comments in rehearsal and generally say, "Just practice!" But do they know how to practice? Have we taught them? Do they have a prescribed order, time parameters, and an organizational framework? Remember, the conductor serves as the bridge from the beginning band student to the person deemed an artist. In other words, our students are a reflection of what we teach them.

Motivating students to practice is one of the hardest aspects of our job. Students must understand that appropriate, meaningful practice is an ongoing process that should evolve into a way of life, much like homework, eating, and sleeping. But you can't ask students to practice something they don't know how to do. It's not possible, and it's certainly not effective. In fact, I don't think it's wise to ask students to practice at all without showing them *how* to practice. Students need a model for good practice habits, they need to feel that the time is well spent, and they need to feel that their practice time yields tangible improvement.

Here is an elementary example of *how* to structure practice. We will get more specific later:

- Stretch
- Breathing exercises
- Listening to a few minutes of your favorite artist on your instrument

**Warm-up to include:** (use a metronome and tuner)
- Mouthpiece buzzing or long tones
- Play a middle register note with the best sound possible and try to replicate it on other notes in different registers
- Remington exercises
- Whole-tone scale
- Attack and release patterns
- Scale studies / Clarke studies / chromatic, thirds, fourths, etc.
- Lip slurs / finger exercises / register and overtone exercises
- Dynamic exercises
- Articulation exercises
- High and low register exercises

This list is not intended to establish a definitive way to practice or warm-up but to simply suggest that if students don't have a model for their practice sessions, they will simply pick up their instrument and start making bad sounds. If **perfect practice makes perfect**, then no model for practicing could certainly be described as "101 ways to practice sounding badly." Putting an instrument together with no pre-practice plan is a poor habit that doesn't get the mind, body, or soul ready to make music.

For the main part of the practice session, it is important to give your students guidelines for how to make their time effective and meaningful. Here are a few examples:

- Start passages slowly with the metronome and play them perfectly at some speed before increasing the tempo.
- Practice technical sixteenth passages by utilizing different rhythm sets, such as dotted-eighth sixteenth, two sixteenth-eighth, to establish muscle memory.
- Practice individual Components of Playing, starting with The Four T's (timing, tune, tone, technique), and then move to rhythm, dynamics, articulations, etc.
- After practicing each component individually, establish a performance where all are played simultaneously.
- Record yourself and assess your performance on a regular basis, especially during sight-reading sessions and mock audition preparations.
- Remember that a few minutes of quality practice is better than any amount of bad practice.

Now it's your turn. Take a moment and write out a plan for *how* you want your students to practice.

_____

_____

_____

_____

_____

_____

_____

## Scale Study Sequence

Scale work is one of the best ways to develop technique. Whether the scales are major or minor, chromatic, whole tone, thirds, or one of the modes, scale study is musical aerobics that needs to be a part of a musician's daily diet. As important as this aspect of playing is to musicians-in-training, we all have students who struggle with learning even basic scale requirements. Here are a few suggestions and techniques for helping students master scales.

- Teach the order of sharps and flats.
- Teach enharmonic notes for mastery.
- Teach accurate transpositions and make sure there is no confusion between concert pitch and their pitch.
- Teach rules for key signatures, whether major or minor.
- Teach the concepts of relative major and minor.
- Teach the proper spelling of scales, accounting for every letter of the musical alphabet (when applicable).
- Teach the chromatic scale enharmonically correct with sharps ascending and flats descending.

There are several teaching techniques to help students master scales. One is the **inversion principle** for major scales. It works this way: If a student knows a basic scale like B♭ but doesn't know B Major, have the student make the flats into naturals and the naturals into sharps to produce the B Major scale. If you write it out on the board, students can easily see where the sharps go because they are inserted on all the natural notes of the B♭ scale. Try this technique on several scales yourself and you'll see that it works.

### The Inversion Principle

| ♭ | | | ♭ | | | | ♭ |
|---|---|---|---|---|---|---|---|
| B | C | D | E | F | G | A | B |

| n | | | n | | | | n |
|---|---|---|---|---|---|---|---|
| B | C | D | E | F | G | A | B |
| | # | # | | # | # | # | |

Another useful application of the inversion principle is determining the number of sharps or flats in a scale. When comparing sharp scales to their flat counterparts, the number must equal seven. Let me explain…The G scale has one sharp. Since the number must add up to seven, the G♭ scale must have six flats. Let's try another. The B♭ scale has two flats, so the B scale should have how many sharps? The answer is five because, again, the number must add up to seven. This is a great teaching tool for young students, and it creates a "lightbulb" moment toward their understanding of key signatures.

Another teaching technique is to use **visual aids**. When using the visual aid for the E scale (shown on the next page), the ledges on each end house the e's, the "peace signs" represent the pairs of sharps shown on the next page, and the thumbs represent the two adjacent naturals. If proceeding from left to right, the scale would read: 2 sharps, 2 naturals, 2 sharps—E. If proceeding from right to left: 2 sharps, 2 naturals, 2 sharps—E.

- Ask students, "What note in the middle of the B scale is natural?"
- Ask students, "What note in the middle of the F# scale is natural?"

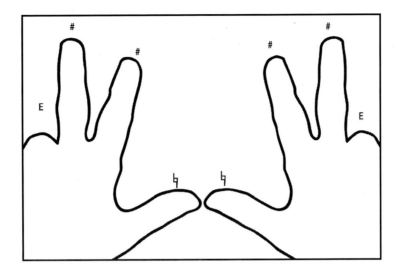

Effective teaching strategies are the key to improving any band. These strategies allow a dialogue to take place that serves as a jumping off point for truly making music. It's easy to say louder, softer, faster, slower...but *how* you teach the various Components of Playing is an investment in your students' musical future.

## Chapter Checklist:

Why are successful teaching strategies so important...

## CALL TO ACTION!

- These techniques will dramatically improve your effectiveness and your ensemble's performance.

- These techniques will fill your rehearsals with vocabulary conducive to music making.

# Chapter Four

## Assessing for Mastery

In *Habits of a Successful Band Director* (GIA, 2006), I started the chapter on assessment by stating, "The notion of giving an A to everyone in band is hogwash!" My comment was in response to directors who give only a participation grade of A or who think, "They've worked really hard this semester so I'll give them all an A." I think everyone would agree that you don't reward someone just for showing up at the door. However, I did not mean to imply that it was all about the grade either. Grading, in and of itself, is a man-made creation. Someone invented the letters we use to provide feedback to students…and did we actually leave out "E" so we could have the joy of writing "F" for Failure? Giving a letter grade is mainly to measure one person's performance against another or a student's performance against a predetermined standard.

Effective assessment should be designed to do two things. The first is to move students from point A to point B within the sequence of learning designed for them. Effective assessment should free students to be able to make mistakes and learn from them. This learning is the mechanism by which students can improve their work. The second thing effective assessment should do is to define that "Aha" moment when students actually get it—mastery. Effective assessment tells us whether students have gotten it. Teaching for mastery enables students to feel that they are learning concepts on a permanent basis and can use the information any time, as needed. In a performance-based class, effective assessment causes students to want to become better on their instruments and provides valuable information to the teacher as to the appropriate skill level of each player.

## Key Practice #3:
## Evaluate mastery through differentiated assessment.

# Types of Assessment

Here is a list of various types of assessment that can be utilized in a performance-based class:

- Rubric (both student and teacher) – comparing work or performance to a standard
- Rating scale
- Checklist
- Verbal critique
- Written critique
- Written tests
- Recorded performance
- Student self-assessment
- Student-centered assessment
- Weighted differentiated instruction
- Live performance reports

This list contains a plethora of specific assessment strategies, each of which you can tailor to fit specific needs within your program. Regardless of which strategy you use, students need feedback regarding their work, and this is one of the most important components of performance-based assessment. This can be in the form of returning a teacher-generated rubric, a verbal critique, a written critique, or a simple email. In addition, students need aural examples of exceptional work (tone quality and other components) prior to giving a performance-based playing assignment. This can be in the form of recordings of exceptional work, demonstrating appropriate criteria, or providing a checklist that would deem work as exceptional. In *Habits of a Successful Band Director* (GIA, 2006), the following types of assessment were also discussed:

- The Four T's Assessment (Appendix A)
- The Three-Tiered Assessment Model (Appendix B)
- Student Self-Assessment Form
- Individual Performance Rubrics (Appendices C and D)

Let's look at a few new ways to bring effective assessment into your rehearsal setting.

**SmartMusic:**

SmartMusic is a wonderful new assessment tool that is cutting edge in its approach. The only requirements for SmartMusic are a computer with internet capabilities, a microphone, and a subscription to the program. (A foot pedal is optional.)

SmartMusic functions as a play-along track for students, but it has many incredible features. It provides immediate feedback by showing correct notes and rhythms, you can set the accompaniment at any speed without loss of pitch, and you can also set the accompaniment to follow the performer. SmartMusic has a vast library of exercises, method books, and works for full ensemble. They are literally adding band titles every month. In addition, you can upload virtually any Finale file into SmartMusic, and with a little tweaking, the program offers some of the same features as the music in their online library.

The advantages of SmartMusic are numerous, but the best feature for educators is the online grade book, which allows the director to preset certain features when assigning a playing test. When a student is finished recording the playing test, the grade is submitted and automatically goes into the grade book. For instance, you may ask your students to play twenty-four measures of *Molly on the Shore* for a grade. Before giving the assignment, you would go to the SmartMusic online gradebook (called Impact) and preset the desired requirements, such as acceptable tempo and percentages of correct notes. Once established, the students can't change the preset requirements. To prepare for the assignment, students would use the Practice Mode (an invaluable tool) to help them establish good practice habits. This feature allows students to change the tempo to a slower speed, establish practice loops of difficult passages, and do a trial run of the assignment prior to submission. As students perform, they follow a cursor that gives them immediate feedback by displaying correct notes in green and mistakes in red.

The limitation of SmartMusic is that it only evaluates correct notes and rhythms. You would need to use other assessment methods to evaluate other components of playing. However, it is a great assessment tool to add to your arsenal. There is also a provision within the SmartMusic program to send return e-mails to your students so you can provide teacher feedback about their performance.

**Okay—Give Everyone an "A":**

In the last few years, I've given my seniors a final assignment. The premise of the final assignment is that they are to make a recording of how they want to be remembered as a musician. I tell them that it must be their best work and that I might play their recording in future years for my students. The recording must be between one and four minutes, can be any genre, and must be something they're proud to leave behind. They can perform a movement of a concerto or their favorite piece of music, or they can improvise with Jamie Aebersold. And, oh…if they turn in the assignment on time and meet the criteria for giving their best effort, they will receive an "A." No rubric, no evaluation of each component, no feedback—they will get an "A."

I began to notice after the second year of doing this that my students were doing their best work of the year for this assignment. They were taking more care to get it right, spending much more time and energy on being musical (really musical), and were taking pride in their finished product. They were also being creative with literature selection, which was rewarding in itself. What was it about this approach that yielded better results? Was it the assurance of an "A"? Was it because it was the last assignment? Or was it the threat of future students hearing their work?

I believe students produced better work because the criteria freed them from failure or judgment. It opened their minds to the possibility of what defined their best work and was geared specifically to each student rather than comparing them with other students. The process was void of competition and the stress of playing in front of the class. It allowed students time to explore various musical possibilities and encouraged them to work at their highest level.

I began to experiment with other students in grades nine through eleven using a similar premise. The end-of-year final assignment is to write a paper stating what kind of player they are going to be during the next year. They are to be specific about how they plan to improve and give many insightful details about their journey of self-discovery. They should include goals and a specific plan for attaining them. If they are taking private lessons, I encourage them to involve their instructor so they can work together to make all of this happen. They also have to prepare a pre- and post-recording demonstrating improvement. And…if they turn the assignment in on time and meet the established criteria for dreaming about their future, they will receive an "A." Again, this approach yielded great success.

This type of assignment is called **student-centered assessment**. Basically, this means that the role of the director is to find the best within each individual student and bring it out. The teacher's job is to help students achieve their highest musical potential, not to set up hoops for them to jump through.

In my experience, this type of assessment works really well, but it is just that—one type of assessment. I don't believe it can be used exclusively as the sole means to evaluate. I also believe a certain amount of student comparison is necessary in our world. In a performance-based class, you can't totally abandon the idea of providing teacher feedback about a student's performance. Rubrics and teacher feedback enable students to troubleshoot their own playing and receive tangible information on how to improve. However, wouldn't it be cool if all students had a logical say in what constituted their "A"? They might be willing to work a little harder if they could see and hear tangible results as part of the improvement process.

After using this approach for a couple of years, one of my students performed in the Honor Orchestra of America with one of my former teachers, Ben Zander, as conductor. The student introduced himself to Mr. Zander and relayed my best wishes. At the end of the weekend, Mr. Zander gave my student a book to bring to me. It was a signed copy of his wonderful book entitled *The Art of Possibility* (Penguin Group, 2002). In the book, Mr. Zander refers to student-centered learning as "giving everyone an A." He states:

The practice of *giving the A* allows the teacher to line up with her students in their efforts to produce the outcome, rather than lining up with the standards against these students…The freely granted A expresses a vision of partnership, teamwork, and relationship. It is for wholeness and functionality, in the awareness that for each of us, excess stone may still hide the graceful form within.

These are powerful words for us to consider and gets us back to the definition of effective assessment moving students from point A to point B. Although each student may start at different points on the track, this type of assessment keeps every student moving forward toward their journey of becoming a musician.

**Three-Tiered Assessment Model:**

One of the assessment types presented in *Habits of a Successful Band Director* (GIA, 2006) is the **three-tiered assessment model**. This model is also based on the idea of taking students where they are (on the track) and moving them forward. I've received many questions about this type of assessment, and people seem interested in how it works, so I have sought to provide more specific information in this book about constructing an effective three-tiered assessment model.

The three-tiered assessment model is based on developing three levels of assessment. The three levels, which should cover the ability ranges of 90% of your students from strongest to weakest, are **Master Musician**, **Advanced Musician**, and **Intermediate Musician** (although you can call the three levels anything you like). Within each level is a bulleted component (example: a "scale" component). As you develop your assessment, it may look like this:

**Master Musician**
- All twelve major scales and the three forms of minor in the following keys: B♭, F, C, G, D, A, and E

**Advanced Musician**
- All twelve major scales for the full range of the instrument

**Intermediate Musician**
- Nine scales in the following keys: B♭, E♭, A♭, D♭, G, C, F, D, and A

Then you may choose to add a solo component. The component can be whatever you like, but it needs to fit your program, address your students needs, and should be in three tiered levels. The solo component may look like this:

### Master Musician
- All twelve major scales and the three forms of minor in the following keys: B♭, F, C, G, D, A, and E
- Two contrasting movements from a major solo work written for your instrument

### Advanced Musician
- All twelve major scales for the full range of the instrument
- One complete movement of a concerto or sonata

### Intermediate Musician
- Nine scales in the following keys: B♭, E♭, A♭, D♭, G, C, F, D, and A
- Your All-State etude or any approved solo, grade III or higher

You may continue to add component bullets in the same manner with the same criteria. There are several advantages to using this system of assessment:

- It allows students to pick the level at which they're most comfortable  by allowing for differentiated instruction, regardless of their entry level into the program.
- Students who have both strengths and weaknesses in their playing can mix-and-match levels for a grade.
- Students with weak skills but big hearts can attempt to move up levels after completing their expected level of difficulty for extra credit; they get really excited when they move up levels.
- Top-level students can function at the highest level of expectation.
- The Master Musician level can serve as the defining criteria for "Honors" credit.

The grading scale for this type of assessment is weighted based on the component and is devised each time you make a three-tiered assessment model. You may assign points to each bullet much like a rubric, or you can establish benchmarks based on the three levels. Example: We have three concert bands in our program. To establish initial benchmarks, we may say that the members of the top ensemble must successfully complete everything in the Master Musician level to be considered for a grade of 100. Likewise, the second band must function at the Advanced Musician level, and the third band at the Intermediate Musician level.

After establishing the benchmark, a weighted system is needed in case students decide to mix levels. This would include extra credit for students in the lower levels who are attempting to move up. An example (using the benchmarks above) would be a student in the second band who elects to do a **solfege** component at the Intermediate level while doing the **solo** component at the Master level.

With that said, how do you combine the concepts of student-centered assessment, teacher feedback, and using a rubric (comparing performance to a standard) to devise an effective assessment strategy? List your ideas:

_____

_____

_____

_____

_____

_____

_____

_____

_____

_____

_____

# Chapter Checklist:

- The primary means of assessment in a performance-based class is the rubric.

- The three-tiered assessment model can be used as a means of effective differentiated instruction.

- Several methods of self-assessment can be integral to student progress if the students are willing to record themselves and listen with a critical ear.

- SmartMusic is a wonderful teaching tool to aid in the students' ability to establish good practice habits.

- Student-centered assessment is a partnership between the teacher and student, which establishes an atmosphere of cooperation and pushes the student toward achieving his or her highest musical potential.

# Chapter Five

## Making Music

Could one spend time teaching the various Components of Playing and never make music? Is it within the realm of possibility that your band could play in time, in tune, with a great sound and loads of technique, and never really capture the soul of the music or the essence of the composer? Is it possible to play and never create magic? The answer to all of the above is—absolutely! The information that has now become the **Habits of Success Plan** is totally useless if we do not realize that it is all a means to an end. Once the tool chest is full of concepts like the Four T's, Components of Playing, and various teaching strategies, it is at that point that we abandon the technique of it all and strive to use these tools to communicate through the language of music. As director, it is our job to equip our students with enough options in their musical toolboxes to function as musicians. Consequently, this allows them to take out the appropriate tool at the appropriate time, and make music.

## Key Practice #4:
## Cross the threshold from teaching strategies to music making.

This brings us to the question: Are we teaching musical concepts? Back in the 1990s, Larry Blocher, Bentley Shellahamer, and Richard Greenwood conducted a research study as part of their graduate work at Florida State University. They examined rehearsal video from directors in the state of Florida with the goal of establishing how much rehearsal time was spent teaching musical concepts. For the sake of their study, they defined teaching musical concepts as the band director "making students aware of, having an understanding of, and/or demonstrating the ability to transfer musical concepts." In their initial study, they evaluated 20-minute video segments and determined that less than 3% of rehearsal time was being spent teaching musical concepts. Wow! I remember the first time I read this study in a research journal and felt a true personal conviction. My immediate reaction was... that might be me.

As any good researcher would do, they then decided to expand the study to include other subgroups. They included student teachers, directors from seven states deemed as outstanding and, finally, college and university directors. Surely a couple of these subgroups would cause the results of the initial findings to go way up, right? What actually happened was that when they combined the findings of all four subgroups, less than 2% of rehearsal time was actually spent teaching musical concepts.

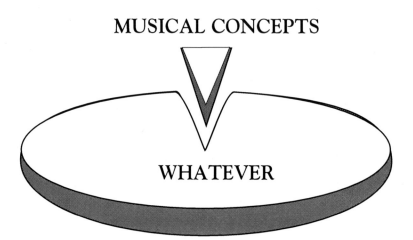

I've quoted this study many times, and the results still astound me. What a challenge to each of us to put music making at the forefront of our teaching experience.

The band director *is* the bridge from the beginning band student to the person deemed an artist.

## Could Someone Please Define Music Making?

I was leading a teacher in-service a couple of years ago and got to a strategic point in the presentation when a question came from the back of the room. The person, who I didn't know personally but who knew had been teaching for many years, posed what I perceived to be a very disturbing question. He said, "Could you please define music making?" He went on to add, "I've been teaching for 27 years and I just simply haven't found this nirvana you keep talking about." Well, at that point I was offended. How could someone who had been in the profession for 27 years not know what music making was all about? The worse part was my response. I said, "Well, you know" (when you start a sentence with "you know," you don't really know)…"it's when the conductor's emoting and the students are emoting, and everybody's emoting…" Can you believe I said that? That was my answer! I got in the car after the workshop, looked in the rearview mirror, and said to myself, "Well, that was a brilliant answer that changed that man's life." Right then and there, I pulled out a piece of paper and began to write down phrases and comments I use within my own teaching process to address music making. During the five-hour drive home, I wrote down quotes and philosophical ideas that promoted music making, and when I pulled into my driveway, I had a nice little list of teaching prompts. Here are a few basic truths about musicianship and phrasing that I put down on paper that day:

**Thoughts About Phrasing and Musicianship:**

Musical Tips:
- Long notes should have direction—they should intensify or decrescendo.
- Phrases should have peaks and valleys, arrival points, and weighted notes (agogic).
- Carry over (connect) phrases and don't breathe at inappropriate places.
- If a line is repeated, do something different with it the second time.
- Find tension and release points.
- Musical moments usually take longer to build than they do to pull away.
- In many styles, short notes lead to long notes.

Extramusical Stimuli:
- It's what's *not* on the page that makes the music.
- Use "mood" words to establish style and ambiance.
- Assign words to entire musical phrases to help establish meaning and purpose.
- Persichetti said, "Music is either dancing or singing."
- It's what happens between the notes that makes the music come alive.

Philosophical Prompts:
- Trust your soul to feel and express the music—be musical! Tell a musical story with passion and conviction.
- The conductor's blood must drip with musical conviction, both to the players and the audience.
- Try to discover music in every phrase.
- Unlike a painting or sculpture, music can be recreated again and again, with new meaning and understanding.
- The paper and ink don't make the music; instruments make no sounds on their own—the soul creates the music.
- Music must be interpreted to the point that the performance is said to be *artistic* and the performers, *artists*.

These bullets are designed to establish a vocabulary and a culture for music making. These musical truths are much different from the Components of Playing list in that they cause the performers to feel and interpret the notes and ink on the page. It's a different mind set than being "in tune," playing "in time," or executing the correct articulation. It's a form of musical communication, a language in and of itself. This list can be used as a checklist, or it can be shared as part of your daily teaching during fundamentals time. Our rehearsal halls should be filled with this type of dialogue. However, it is very important to note that you can't put the cart before the horse. You can't establish this dialogue without first mastering the Components of Playing. In other words, it doesn't matter how a phrase is played if the tone quality stinks.

Let's take a look at each of these **musical tips**—these "thoughts" about musicianship:

- **Long notes should have direction—they should intensify or decrescendo.** It's a pretty simple concept to understand that notes should have direction. Some long notes should go over the barline with intensity. Ben Zander quoted in his book, *The Art of Possibility* (Penguin Group, 2002):

   > Where is the electric socket for possibility [music making]…? It's just there over the bar line, where the bird soars. We can join it by finding the tempo and lean our bodies to the music; dare to let go of the edges of ourselves…participate!

   Long notes can be *shaped* in a myriad of ways with various dynamic shadings. What can the player do with just one note? The answer lies in the notion that you must always have a musical opinion, and how you get from one note to the next is where the music happens. Having a note decay is just as important as giving it intensity.

- **Phrases should have peaks and valleys, arrival points, and weighted notes (agogic).** Just as long notes should have direction, so should phrases. Peaks and valleys refer to the musical contour of the line. They are executed with unwritten dynamic inflection and follow the tessitura of the line in many cases. Arrival points refer to those places where the musical line takes us. Some arrival points are part of the smaller phrase structure, while others are planned out by the composer as part of the larger scheme of the work.

- **Carry over phrases and don't breathe in inappropriate places.** With regard to phrasing and musicianship, it is important to instill the idea that music should be played as if the barline doesn't exist. Barlines are there only to organize meter. They are not phrase indicators and audience members should not hear them. The *musical line* is of utmost importance, and musical decisions need to be made based on this. Musical line can also refer to how you approach and leave arrival points. When playing long phrases, it may be necessary to stagger breathe so as not to break the line.

The next several bullets are not absolutes and don't necessarily work in every musical style:

- **If a line is repeated, do something different with it the second time.** One of the interpretive decisions the conductor must make is the idea of how to treat repeated figures or phrases in music. These decisions are sometimes based on the time period, genre, and style of the music. There may be times in music when a figure is played loud the first time and soft the second time, much like an "echo." This concept can also be applied to performing a march, where decisions are made about repeating a particular strain. This also works in a Passacaglia, where a theme reoccurs throughout an entire work. Whatever the situation, you should have ideas about keeping the music interesting and fresh.

- **Find tension and release points.** Take your right hand and tightly grab your left bicep. Now let go, as if you're getting your blood pressure taken. This analogy of tension and release is a great way to introduce the concept to students. Tension and release points happen in many ways and forms. They can come in the form of a musical "sigh," can be played as a suspension, can be expressed in the form of agogic weight, or can be expressed in a much broader framework within the music. Musical tension always resolves to a point of contentment, and this conflict or dichotomy in music should be sought out as part of the journey you wish to share with listeners.

- **Musical moments usually take longer to build than they do to pull away.** Another way of saying this is: Good things come to those who wait. There are so many analogies to demonstrate this concept. A Hollywood kiss is much more dramatic and satisfying if it takes a while to connect. Likewise, music is much more dramatic and satisfying if you slowly build to the climax of the work. I've always been a fan of watching high divers jump, whether off the cliffs in Mexico or as part of an amusement park show. The drama comes from the diver waiting for the conditions to be just right before taking the plunge. Sometimes they even act as if they are going to jump only to stop just before takeoff, further adding to the suspense of the moment. Another analogy would be the image or action of climbing a mountain. There is real effort in reaching the summit, but the view is dramatic and satisfying, followed by a much easier descent to the ground. A wonderful crescendo can be a musical homerun if paced in just the right way. The suspense comes from stretching the beats prior to the arrival point and saving the crescendo for just the right moment. The next downbeat is given just over the barline and the music soars!

- **In many styles, short notes lead to long notes.** This concept has to do with both line and agogic weight. The most logical example is when pickup notes lead to longer notes on the downbeat. I use the analogy of rocks skipping across the water and then, *plop!* The long note receives the weight. The short notes are given direction, while the long note serves as an arrival point. In many styles, longer notes receive more weight (in general) than their shorter counterparts. All notes should have some type of direction; this concept is a microcosm of the overall interpretation of the work.

The **extramusical stimuli** and **philosophical prompts** are a little more aesthetic and personal in nature. Examples of mood words, for instance, may have more of an impact if they are something the students can relate to. If the analogy were, "This should sound like palm trees swaying in the South Pacific," then the students probably need to have been in a climate conducive to palm trees swaying in the breeze.

Take a moment to react to the following statements and write what these philosophical prompts mean to you.

It's what's *not* on the page that makes the music.

_____

_____

Use mood words to establish style and ambiance (give an example).

_____

_____

Assign words to entire musical phrases to help establish meaning and purpose.

_____

_____

To help with this, let me give you an example. Rodney Winther, the incredible conductor from the Cincinnati Conservatory of Music, was working with our ensemble. We were performing *Gumsucker's March* by Grainger, and the students were having trouble with both inflection and line. Rodney began to tell a story about my son, Thomas. In the story, he sang the phrase, "Thomas, we really think that you're cute"…Thomas was just a toddler and pretty adorable (if I say so myself). This phrase was over the melody from *Gumsucker's*. As the story continued, the phrase, which began with "Thomas," kept introducing a new idea. After Rodney's story, the band played the melodic line again. This time there was wonderful line, inflection, and nuance.

Music is either dancing or singing.

_____

_____

It's what happens from note to note that makes the music come alive.

_____

_____

Tell a musical story with passion and conviction.

_____

_____

The conductor's blood must drip with musical conviction.

_____

_____

Try to discover music in every phrase.

_____

_____

Music can be recreated again and again with new meaning and understanding.

_____

_____

The paper and ink don't make the music—the soul creates the music.

_____

_____

Music must be interpreted to the point that the performance is said to be *artistic* and the performers, *artists*.

_____

_____

Our ensemble was very fortunate to have Dale Clevenger, principal horn of the Chicago Symphony Orchestra, perform the Franz Strauss *Nocturno* as part of our performance at the Midwest Clinic in 2007. A few months prior to the performance, Mr. Clevenger flew to South Carolina to rehearse the work with the band. Our conversations were mini-music lessons in themselves, but he said something that stuck out in my mind as incredibly profound. He said that Daniel Barenboim once told the principal players of the Chicago Symphony, "You are some of the finest players in the world. You can play anything that I ask you to play. I just wish that you would do it before I asked."

To me, that was as practical an application of teaching music making as any that I'd heard. Once you equip the musical toolbox, students should not only be free to make music, but they should be urged (if not pleaded with) to express themselves prior to being asked. After all, this is what defines music education—communicating through the language of music. Interpretations will always change, but the worst interpretation is none at all.

What are other sayings, thoughts, or concepts you use with your students?

_____

_____

_____

_____

## Music-Making Exercise:

As part of the preparation for our Midwest Clinic performance, we reached a point where all of the "nuts and bolts" information had been put on the table and most decisions about phrasing and interpretation had been reached. The problem was the students weren't expressing themselves musically, and they were certainly not communicating anything with emotion. At that point, we began doing an exercise in rehearsal to help facilitate exactly what needed to happen to effectively say something, musically.

The first time I did this, I asked three students to create a musical conversation. I chose my principal alto saxophonist to be student one and then added a flutist and a percussionist on marimba. I asked them to use the first five notes of the Ab concert scale and to use only quarters, half notes, and whole notes for their rhythmic choices. I then asked student one to begin and end the conversation on tonic "do." I also asked the students to pick a slow tempo and to genuinely try to express something to one another and the other students in the room. Their segments were limited to no more than eight measures in length. Student one began the conversation and played an eloquent four-bar phrase. The flute player instinctively picked up the line and developed the conversation. The student on marimba used four-mallet technique to create a beautiful combination of rolls and melodic line, which was a continuation of what had already been established. The conversation lasted for about two minutes, and then student one produced a wonderful cadence and ended on "do." The room was at first quiet because everyone was simply stunned. These students had created and crafted beautiful music from their hearts. Softly, a student began to shuffle on the floor, and then another student clapped, and the room burst forth with energy. Everyone who heard or participated in the experience felt something meaningful, and the concept of communicating through music became real and magical. From that point forward, the ensemble played with real musical conviction—they wanted to say something musically. They were also very eager to do the exercise and wanted to do it as often as I would let them.

# Growing as an Artist

I want to pause a moment and make a statement I strongly believe to be true. Just as we must never stop learning, **we must also never stop growing as artists.** True artistry is like a fine wine—it matures with age. Bruno Walter states in *Of Music and Music Making* (W. W. Norton & Company, 1961):

> ...that the value of a conductor's artistic achievement is to a high degree dependent upon his human qualities and capacities; the seriousness of his moral convictions, the richness of his emotional life, the breadth of his mental horizon, in short, his personality, has a decisive effect on his achievements; if his personality is unable to fulfill the spiritual demands of the works he performs, his interpretations will remain unsatisfactory although their musical execution may be exemplary.

When I was a senior in high school, I attended the Brevard Music Center summer program in the mountains of North Carolina. I completely enjoyed the experience except for one aspect of our required concert series—the operas. As a seventeen-year-old, I detested sitting through a three-hour opera. I enjoyed the musicals, but the operas were pure torture. I just didn't understand all of the hullabaloo. In my seventeen-year-old mind, it was a bunch of non-musical warbling. Then a funny thing happened on the way to becoming a musician. For the next four summers, I was asked to return to Brevard as a counselor and play as a member of the BMC Orchestra, which meant I got to play in the pit for the operas. As I grew as an artist and began performing the music, I realized that some of the greatest music in the world comes from the opera repertoire. I love the opera music of Puccini, Verdi, and Mozart, and some of the finest conductors I've had the privilege of playing under were the really good opera conductors. (Mark Flynt of the New York City Opera is especially amazing!) Experiencing the music made all of the difference in the world. As educators, we have the responsibility to experience all types of music and immerse ourselves in the study and listening of music. Warren Bennis wrote in *On Becoming a Leader* (Basic Book, 2003), "Leaders differ from others in their constant appetite for knowledge and experience, and as their worlds widen and become more complex, so too do their means of understanding." Don't stifle your appetite for learning and growing.

Another such growth experience came when I was a young director. I attended the Bands of America National Concert Band Festival one March in Indianapolis and listened to a wonderful high school band perform the first movement of the Hindemith Symphony. After listening to the performance, I looked at my wife and said, "Don't ever let me program that with a high school group. It's just too far out there for high school kids." What I really meant was that it was too far out there for my mind and soul to grasp at that point in my career. I have since not only programmed the work but continue to study its many layers. Hindemith's sense of orchestration, counterpoint, thematic structure, and pure genius is second to none in this masterwork. It is really unfortunate that we don't have more masterworks from his pen for the wind orchestra.

I mention all of this because many in the wind band world are quick to call something esoteric, when in fact, they ought to dig a little deeper and find merit. I'll be the first to admit that there are many "duds" written for the wind band and lots of stuff that should end up in the trashcan. However, as music educators, it is our job to saturate our musical minds with great works from masterful composers. If you haven't listened to Brahms, Mahler, Hindemith, Persichetti, or Grainger in a while, take some personal time and revisit the classics.

## Concert Curriculum

Curriculum is an interesting word in the concert rehearsal setting. Part of our curriculum should be the methods by which we teach the fundamentals of playing and developing an ensemble sound, and any materials we use to teach musical concepts. The foundation of all of this, however, is the literature we select to perform with our ensembles. I cannot stress how important this piece of the puzzle is in defining your band program. The highest-quality literature is what your students take with them into their adult lives. Each year, I write a letter to the seniors in our band program. A portion of the letter reads:

> I hope that you will continue to play your instrument after high school. College band is obviously the best place to do this (and they usually will pay you to do it), but there are certainly other avenues. Community bands, jazz combos, local bands that gig around town, forming your own chamber music group...these are just a few examples. In addition, I hope that you will go to concerts (any type of music), but especially hope that you will take the knowledge of the composers and music that you know into your adult life. I hope that one day your child will ask, "How do you know that piece of music?" and you'll be able to answer, "Because I learned it and performed it in band.

I am a huge proponent of performing orchestral transcriptions for band. It may be the only place that some of our students will hear works by Mozart, Stravinsky, Beethoven, Berlioz, or Elgar. I applaud the work of people like Joseph Kreines and Jay Bocook, who constantly strive to put orchestral works into the hands of our band students. I also support works written strictly for the wind band and have been a part of several commissioning projects. It is vitally important that we keep our medium thriving with commissions of high-quality literature by the very finest composers.

The following is in no way intended to be a definitive list for large ensemble programming. However, I am often asked by my colleagues to suggest high-quality works. In compiling this list, I strongly believe in these two statements:

- Choose literature that allows for applying and reinforcing musical concepts.
- Conceptual teaching promotes transfer from fundamentals to music-making.

**Music Selection List:**

### Middle School Band

| | |
|---|---|
| *Ahrirang* | Garofalo/Whaley |
| *Air for Band* | Erickson |
| *Allegro, Adagio, and Alleluia* | Akers |
| *Anasazi* | Edmondson |
| *An Occasional Suite* | Handel/Osterling |
| *Barn Dance Saturday Night* | La Plante |
| *Beau Galant* | Telemann/Gordon |
| *Caprice* | Himes |
| *Chester* | Billings/Tolmage |
| *Country Wildflowers* | Daehn |
| *Court Festival* | Byrd/Pearson |
| *Creed* | Himes |
| *Crest of Nobility* | Sheldon |
| *Glorioso* | Smith |
| *Greenwillow Portrait* | Williams |
| *Imaginary Soundscape, No. 2* | Del Borgo |
| *Imperium* | Sweeney |
| *In Dulci Jubilo* | Zdechlik |
| *Music from the Great Hall* | Fenske |
| *Portrait of a Clown* | Ticheli |
| *Prelude and March* | Frackenpohl |
| *Romanza* | Ford |
| *Sarabande and Gavotte* | Corelli/Johnson |
| *Song for Friends* | Daehn |
| *Song for Winds* | Edmondson |
| *The Headless Horseman* | Broege |
| *Theme and Variations* | Broege |
| *The Tempest* | R. Smith |

| | |
|---|---|
| *Train Heading West and Other Outdoor Scenes* | Broege |
| *Two British Folksongs* | Del Borgo |
| *Two Russian Folksongs* | Gingery |
| *Visions on an Old American Tune* | Pegram |

## Younger Band

| | |
|---|---|
| *Alligator Alley* | Daugherty |
| *Amazing Grace* | Ticheli |
| *American Riversongs* | La Plante |
| *Ammerland* | de Haan |
| *As Summer Was Just Beginning* | Daehn |
| *Australian Up-Country Tune* | Grainger |
| *Ave Maria* | Biebl/Cameron |
| *Blessed Are They* | Brahms/Buehlman |
| *Cajun Folk Songs* | Ticheli |
| *Courtly Airs and Dances* | Nelson |
| *Down a Country Lane* | Copland/Patterson |
| *In the Bleak Midwinter* | Holst |
| *Lux Arumque* | Whitacre |
| *March of the Belgian Paratroopers* | Leemans |
| *Old Scottish Melody* | Wiley |
| *On a Hymnsong of Philip Bliss* | Holsinger |
| *Prospect* | La Plante |
| *Romanza* | Ford |
| *Rhosymedre* | Vaughan Williams |
| *Salvation Is Created* | Tchesnekoff/Kreines |
| *Sussex Mummer's Christmas Carol* | Grainger/Kreines |
| *The Crosley March* | Fillmore |
| *Their Blossoms Down* | Hazo |
| *They Led My Lord Away* | Gordon |
| *Three Ayres from Gloucester* | Stuart |
| *Two Grainger Melodies* | Grainger/Kreines |
| *With Quiet Courage* | Daehn |
| *Ye Banks and Braes o' Bonnie Doon* | Grainger |

## Intermediate Level

| | |
|---|---|
| *Allerseelen* | Strauss/Davis |
| *Americans We (March)* | Fillmore |
| *As the Scent of Spring Rain* | Newman |
| *Black Horse Troop (March)* | Sousa/Fennell |
| *Chester* | Schuman |

| | |
|---|---|
| *Children's March* | Grainger |
| *Chorale and Alleluia* | Hanson |
| *Chorale and Shaker Dance* | Zdechlik |
| *Colors and Contours* | Bassett |
| *Easter Monday on the White House Lawn* | Sousa |
| *Elegy for a Young American* | LoPresti |
| *Elsa's Procession to the Cathedral* | Wagner/Cailliet |
| *English Folk Song Suite* | Vaughan Williams |
| *Entry March of the Boyars* | Halvorsen/Fennell |
| *First Suite in Eb* | Holst |
| *Flashing Winds* | Van der Roost |
| *Florentiner (March)* | Fucik |
| *Folk Dances* | Shostakovich/Reynolds |
| *Gallant Seventh (March)* | Sousa |
| *Galop* | Shostakovich/Hunsberger |
| *His Honor (March)* | Fillmore |
| *Inglesina (Little English Girl)* | De Ceese |
| *Irish Tune from County Derry* | Grainger |
| *Klaxon (March)* | Fillmore |
| *Lullaby for Kirsten* | Bassett |
| *March, Op. 99* | Prokofiev |
| *Marriage of Figaro (Overture)* | Mozart/Slocum |
| *O Magnum Mysterium* | Lauridsen/Reynolds |
| *October* | Whitacre |
| *Pageant* | Persichetti |
| *Pas Redouble* | Saint-Saens/Frackenpohl |
| *Pathfinder of Panama (March)* | Sousa/Fennell |
| *Praise to the Lord* | Nelhybel |
| *Prelude in the Dorian Mode* | DeCabezon/Grainger |
| *Prelude, Siciliano, and Rondo* | Arnold/Paynter |
| *Resting in the Peace of His Hands* | Gibson |
| *Second Suite in F* | Holst |
| *Shepherd's Hey* | Grainger |
| *Sinfonia V* | Broege |
| *Song for Band* | Bolcom |
| *Themes from "Green Bushes"* | Grainger/Daehn |
| *Third Suite* | Jager |
| *The Thunderer (March)* | Sousa/Fennell |
| *Toccata* | Frescobaldi/Slocum |
| *Trauersinfonie* | Wagner/Votta |
| *Whip and Spur* | Allen |

**Advanced Level**

| | |
|---|---|
| *A Boy's Dream* | Bocook |
| *Adagietto from Symphony No. 5* | Mahler/Kreines |
| *Aegean Festival Overture* | Makris |
| *…and the mountains rising nowhere* | Schwantner |
| *Armenian Dances, Parts I and II* | Reed |
| *Awayday* | Gorb |
| *Circus Bee* | Fillmore |
| *Colonial Song* | Grainger |
| *Dance of the Jesters* | Tchaikovsky/Hindsley |
| *Danceries* | Hesketh |
| *Divertimento* | Persichetti |
| *Emblems* | Copland |
| *Enigma Variations* | Elgar/Slocum |
| *Festive Overture* | Shostakovich/Hunsberger |
| *Four Scottish Dances* | Arnold/Paynter |
| *George Washington Bridge* | Schuman |
| *Gumsucker's March* | Grainger |
| *Hammersmith* | Holst |
| *Lincolnshire Posy* | Grainger |
| *Minstrels of the Kells* | Welcher |
| *Music for Prague 1968* | Husa |
| *New World Symphony* | Dvorak/Hindsley |
| *Overture to "Candide"* | Bernstein/Grundman |
| *Postcard* | Ticheli |
| *Red Cape Tango* | Daugherty |
| *Russian Christmas Music* | Reed |
| *Selections from "The Danserye"* | Susato/Dunnigan |
| *Sinfonietta* | Dahl |
| *Suite Francaise* | Milhaud |
| *Suite of Old American Dances* | Bennett |
| *Symphonic Metamorphosis* | Hindemith/Wilson |
| *Symphony in Bb* | Hindemith |
| *Symphony No. 2* | Ticheli |
| *Symphony No. 4 ("Finale")* | Tchaikovsky/Hindsley |
| *Symphony No. 6* | Persichetti |
| *Tam o'Shanter* | Arnold/Paynter |
| *The Leaves Are Falling* | Benson |
| *Theme and Variations, Op. 43a* | Schoenberg |
| *The Solitary Dancer* | Benson |
| *Vienna Philharmonic Fanfare* (brass ensemble) | Strauss |

# Marching Curriculum

Since writing *Habits of a Successful Band Director* (GIA, 2006), one of the consistent comments that I've received from people who read the book was, "You didn't include very much about marching band." There is a reason for this. It's not that I am anti-marching band, but I've been a little concerned about the direction marching band has taken in recent years. Marching band is not its own animal (or shouldn't be), but it has certainly turned into a beast. As Roy Holder stated in a recent article in the *NBA Journal*, " 'Marching' is an adjective to band. It's not a noun." It is one of the spokes of the wheel (with concert band as the hub of the wheel), and most of the concepts used in concert band can be directly applied and transferred to the field. One of the facets I feel most passionate about with regard to marching band is that of music programming. I'll concede to the fact that contemporary marching band has caused many to work on the same marching music for three or four months. My comments to this are twofold: First, you should be working on marching music after school and performing concert music during the school day. Second, the marching music should be high-quality literature. As for the former, I would encourage everyone to schedule a concert during October or early November. It will keep you well-grounded in concert music throughout the marching band season.

The collective band community has an awesome responsibility when it comes to appropriate programming for our ensembles. We must select literature that fits the ensemble, and we must select music that has value and is paced appropriately. Nowhere is this more crucial than in the area of marching band. Marching band programming involves a collaboration of so many different elements—arrangers, visual coordinators, student education, physical demands, variety—and it all has to coexist and function simultaneously.

One's philosophy about marching band music needs to evolve from a basic premise: that music, in and of itself, is the language of the soul, and there is no substitute for high-quality music. This premise eliminates the argument as to whether marching music should be predominantly classical, jazz, contemporary, from the band repertoire, or within one particular genre at all. Just as there are great pieces of music within each grade level of concert band literature, there are worthy pieces of music that can be used quite effectively for marching band. The music should speak to the soul and take the listeners on a musical journey.

For marching band, I like to add one additional barometer to the process. Since we generally live with marching music for much longer than we'd like, I ask the question: Does the music lend itself to the teaching process?

- Is there something that can be learned about the composer/artist?
- Will the work allow us to discover other works by the same composer/artist?
- Will the music expose my students to other genres (for instance, choral works)?

- Will the selections allow my students to make music, especially within the realm of things that are not written on the page?
- Will the music allow my students to perfect the various components of playing, or are they simply providing effect?
- If my students were assigned to create program notes for each of our marching band selections, would the notes have depth and meaning?

This barometer is the reason I prefer selecting the music for a marching band show first, not the other way around. I have certainly seen it work when the visual ideas are created first, but it is not my preference. A talented drill designer and a creative guard writer can take any great piece of music and make it visually come to life.

Another crucial component to the marching music process is variety and pacing. If our goal is to take listeners on a musical journey, then it is necessary to create a variety of moods. In addition, it is important that the music allow for coordination of visual and musical ideas. In our program, our rule of thumb is that we want something significant to happen every minute or less within a field show.

A few additional comments…

- **Don't try to be something you're not!** If your program is not known for having a really awesome jazz band, then don't program a jazz show for the field. It's okay to establish a musical identity based on the strengths and philosophy of your program.

- **Don't program music that is too difficult to march to and play.** There's nothing worse than realizing after the fact that you made a bad programming decision. It's not worth the anguish you'll put yourself through.

- **When beginning the initial listening process, it's vitally important to hear and see from the perspective of the guard and percussion.** There are great pieces of music that could be utilized, that could also result in not allowing the guard and percussion to put their best foot forward. Remember that decisions about music must be made with all of the elements coexisting and functioning simultaneously.

- **Think from the perspective of the judge.** Although I think this is the least important attribute of music selection, I do think it is something to consider within the marching band process. Will all music judges think your program contains worthy music choices? If the answer is a definitive *yes*, then you're on the right track. People call me all the time and ask for marching band literature suggestions. I'll sometimes ask, "What did you play last year?" If they say, "The music of Black Sabbath," then I know we're in trouble from the start.

Our goal should always be to make great music! The ultimate goal is to choose music that allows us to proceed through the teaching process to the point that our rehearsal vocabulary addresses, for example, what to do with a long note, how to play a phrase, or tension and release points. As you begin selecting music for marching band, I hope these tips will help lead you to a successful and musical marching season.

## Improving Musicianship through Small Ensembles

I believe one of the very best ways to improve both individual and ensemble musicianship is to play in a chamber ensemble. There are several advantages to playing in a chamber ensemble:

- Students will experience wonderful literature by great composers.
- Students must be musically independent.
- Students will improve their musical communication.
- Students can't hide within the section.
- Ensemble concepts are reinforced and transfer from small to large ensemble.
- It's one of the best ways to develop great players in your program

Also, **chamber music programming dispels the notion of chair placements and gives many students an opportunity to be the star!**

In *Habits of a Successful Band Director* (GIA, 2006), there is a list of possible chamber ensembles along with a myriad of chamber music titles. If you don't have a huge budget for chamber music, you might consider purchasing ensembles contained within a series. By doing this, you may get ten to twenty titles under one cover. For example:

- Woodwind quintet:
    *Ensemble Repertoire for Woodwind Quintet* (Voxman/Hervig)
    *Twenty-two Woodwind Quintets* (Andraud)

- Brass quintet:
    *Canadian Brass Book of Easy Quintets* (Barnes)
    *Canadian Brass Advanced Quintets* (Barnes)
- Clarinet choir:
    *Clarinet Choir Repertoire* (Voxman)

- Saxophone quartet:
    *Quartet Repertoire for Saxophone* (Voxman)
    *Ten Saxophone Quartets* (Teal)

- Percussion ensemble:
  *Percussion Ensemble Collection* (Farberman)    Total: $350.00

By using this method to start your library, every instrument can participate. Euphoniums can play trombone parts, and bass trombones can play tuba parts. I know of one program that uses this method as part of their full band experience.

There are many obstacles to starting a chamber music program, but it is a wonderful investment of time. Here are thoughts regarding implementation:

- There is no time to rehearse—do it anyway!
- Pick a day as "chamber music day."
- Divide rehearsals so part is set aside for chamber music.
- Have students rehearse on their own.
- Hire chamber music coaches.
- Let one ensemble a day out of their normal class rehearsal to practice.
- Assign a student leader for each group.

There are many performance opportunities for chamber ensembles. Here are just a few:

- Solo and ensemble festival
- Collage concert
- Symphonic camp
- Community events
- Local churches
- Nursing homes

Many wonderful institutions of higher learning use some type of chamber music format for their wind ensemble concerts. At New England Conservatory, Frank Battisti would begin many concerts with small ensembles. Concerts would start with a quartet, then an octet, then harmoniemusik instrumentation, brass choir, small ensemble, full ensemble, etc.

I still can't believe I blew the answer to the question, "Could someone please define music making?" However, that one moment was a wonderful growth experience for me because it allowed me to codify the language involved in the music making process.

We'll end this chapter by posing the question to you: Define music making in your own words…

# The definition of music making means...

_____

_____

_____

_____

_____

_____

_____

_____

_____

_____

_____

_____

_____

_____

_____

_____

_____

_____

## Chapter Checklist:

With my apologies to George Michael (you just dated yourself), a great way to remember the pedagogical issues covered in the first five chapters of this book is to remember the following acrostic:

### *WHAM!*

### The Four Key Practices

**1. *W*hat to teach

**2. *H*ow to teach it

**3. *A*ssessment for all learners

**4. *M*usic making

# Chapter Six

# Personal Renewal Time

I am going to assume that you acquired this book because you have the desire to improve. If you believe that one should never stop learning, then you've come to the right place. This chapter is designed to set the stage for your journey of self-discovery and to establish a sense of where you are in evaluating your strengths and weaknesses as a band director. Warren Bennis stated in his classic book, *On Becoming a Leader* (Perseus Publishing, 2003):

> …until you truly know yourself, strengths and weaknesses, know what you want to do and why you want to do it, you cannot succeed in any but the most superficial sense of the word.

Whether you are a college student preparing to enter the teaching profession or a college professor with twenty-five years of experience, there is always room for improvement. You may feel that your weaknesses are administrative, or you may feel that your pedagogical skills are not where you'd like them to be. Regardless of your personal assessment, this chapter enables you to take inventory of your current feelings and thoughts about yourself as a teacher.

A trusted colleague who is a college professor and fine wind conductor recently remarked:

> When you're a high school director, the students want to know more than anything else that you care about them. When you're a college director, students want to know more than anything else that you really know your stuff. They really don't care that much about bonding qualities as much as they base their opinion of you on how well you practice your craft.

It would be rather naïve on my part to assume that everyone reading this text would be in the same state with regard to evaluating his or her own teaching situation. For this reason, it is important that as you read the book, you are constantly formulating a plan for improving various aspects of your program and evaluating how you are teaching the various pedagogical and non-pedagogical concepts within your program.

The goal of this chapter is to begin a process of self-discovery that will lead to real-world applications and solutions. Making notes and recording your thoughts should lead to deeper insights about where you are and where you want to be as a band director. Effectiveness can be learned, and this process of "sharpening the saw" should lead to a deeper, more meaningful teaching experience. The results should empower you to take yourself and your program to a new level of performance.

## Personal Assessment

The future belongs to those who believe in the beauty of their dreams.
—Eleanor Roosevelt

I recently visited my financial planner, and he gave me a little book that was my homework for the visit. The document asked me not only to plan for the financial numbers required to retire with dignity but also to list my dreams, passions, and plans for retirement. It was a great little exercise—and very similar to what you are doing in this chapter and throughout the book. Before you begin with the end in mind, it is important to determine where you are right now. Answer the following questions:

What is your current state of mind regarding your job or entering the workforce?

_Uncertainty - all online  unknowns -_

What were the contributing factors that influenced you in becoming a band director?

_I want kids to experience music & enjoy!_

_____

_____

What do you want to achieve as a band director?

My students leave my program w/
& Appreciation of
an informed love of music

_____

_____

What factors need to be in place for you to achieve your goals?

- positive environment

_____

_____

What type of job scenario do you want to avoid?

- down in the dumps -

_____

_____

_____

**For veteran teachers:**

Looking back on your teaching experiences now, what do you think your students thought of you? Do you believe their thoughts about you were respectful and admired, warranted, unfounded, or lacked understanding?

I think they thought I was fun &
cool. I definitely didn't know enough, but
I had a good co teacher who worked well
with me & the music program

**Note to self:**

Quickly summarize your innermost thoughts about teaching and being a band director, and provide tangible reasons as to why you feel this way:

- I just want kids to experience music -
It's not about me - it's about them

- I knew it would be hard, but sometimes
it's more than I thought -

For some folks, the answer to the previous question is immensely positive, while for others it is an honest source of concern. If your reactions were negative, then evaluate your situation of conflict by posing and answering three simple questions:

1. What is the problem?
2. What is the cause of the problem?
3. What is my proactive solution to the problem?

Tim Lautzenheiser said in a recent leadership workshop, "Any time you think the problem is out there, that is the problem." All of us are quick to place blame on outside forces when, in reality, the first place we should look is in the mirror. Most problems in the teaching profession can be traced back to something we are not doing. Maybe we're not establishing a climate for making music, maybe we're not motivating the kids, maybe we lack the skills to teach certain concepts, maybe we're unclear, or maybe we lack passion for what we're teaching. The one thing we should never do in teaching is to deem ourselves the victim of outside circumstances. Searching for a proactive solution simply means that despite any other circumstance, there is always something we can do to better ourselves or improve a situation…it is a choice we make. We can be proactive despite any obstacle put in front of us.

In doing a personal assessment, apply the above questions to what you currently perceive as the five biggest obstacles you face as a band director. If you're about to enter the profession, try to determine what you think your five greatest obstacles may be.

**PROBLEM #1:** _____

Cause: _____

Proactive
Solution: _____

_____

_____

_____

## PROBLEM #2: _____

Cause: _____

Proactive
Solution: _____

_____

_____

_____

## PROBLEM #3: _____

Cause: _____

Proactive
Solution: _____

_____

_____

_____

## PROBLEM #4: _____

Cause: _____

Proactive
Solution: _____

_____

_____

_____

**PROBLEM #5:** _____

Cause: _____

Proactive
Solution: _____

_____

_____

_____

I hope that while identifying the cause of each problem, you were able to search internally for answers. In Chapter Nine, you will be prompted to develop a professional mission statement. You may want to refer back to your proactive solutions when organizing your thoughts about the mission statement.

## Identify Strengths and Weaknesses

Whether you are a veteran teacher or a novice, you need to know your strengths and weaknesses. You should have a clear idea as to which areas require daily attention and which areas seem to come naturally. For example, my earliest issues were with classroom management and assessment.

Answer the following "yes or no" questions to help clarify your assessment of skills needed on the podium. Elaborate on your answers.

1. Do you communicate well from the podium (cues, head out of the score, eye contact)?   ☐ Yes ☐ No

_____

_____

2. Have you videotaped yourself conducting? If yes, what did you learn?   ☐ Yes ☐ No

_____

_____

3. When you stop, do you clearly communicate your intent?   ☐ Yes ☐ No

_____

_____

4. Are you passionate about making music?   ☐ Yes ☐ No

_____

_____

5. Are you able to reflect the piece (composer's intent) through conducting gestures (indication of phrasing, articulation, dynamics, contradiction of words and gestures)? ☐ Yes ☐ No

_____

_____

6. Are you willing to say, "That was my fault," on the podium? ☐ Yes ☐ No

_____

_____

7. Are you well-prepared for rehearsal? ☐ Yes ☐ No

_____

_____

8. Do you have a soft side while still appearing confident? ☐ Yes ☐ No

_____

_____

9. Are you concise in your trouble-shooting instructions? ☐ Yes ☐ No

_____

_____

10. Do you have techniques for teaching musical concepts
toward mastery? ☐ Yes ☐ No

_____

_____

11. Do you use time wisely? ☐ Yes ☐ No

_____

_____

12. Are you a technician or a musician on the podium? ☐ Yes ☐ No

_____

_____

Answer the following questions by identifying your greatest strengths and weaknesses as a director for the various listed topics:

**Organizational Skills:**

What is your greatest strength?

_____

_____

Your weakness?

_____

_____

**Classroom Management:**

What is your greatest strength?

_____

_____

Your weakness?

_____

_____

**Professionalism:**

What is your greatest strength?

_____

_____

Your weakness?

_____

_____

**Personal Issues:**
(that may enhance or interfere with your ability to be effective)

What is your greatest strength?

_____

_____

Your weakness?

_____

_____

**Note to Self:**
Summarize your thoughts and identify several skills necessary to begin the process of turning your weaknesses into strengths.

_____

_____

_____

_____

_____

_____

## Chapter Checklist:

- You must honestly assess your own strengths and weaknesses, and establish proactive solutions for problem areas.

- Your solutions must be tangible reactions to issues. For example: If your weakness is classroom discipline, a solution would be implementing Harry Wong's procedures for classroom management.

- Never lose sight of what it was that brought you into the profession, and always have a plan for conquering what might cause you to leave it.

# Chapter Seven

# Structure Equals Learning

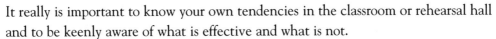

It really is important to know your own tendencies in the classroom or rehearsal hall and to be keenly aware of what is effective and what is not.

About fifteen years ago, three researchers tried to determine the components of teaching that were most crucial in the classroom by reviewing thousands of documents (Wang, Haertel, Walberg, "What Helps Students Learn," from *Educational Leadership*, pp. 74–79). They attempted to put them in some type of rank from most to least important. What they discovered should be a lesson to us all. They determined that **classroom management** was the most important component of student learning. Why had no one told me this *before* I started teaching? We must be acutely aware of our own personal tendencies as a director and realize that classroom management is the number one factor that influences student learning. As one of my colleagues said, "You gotta get 'em quiet and their fannies in the seats—then you might have a chance at teachin 'em something!"

Our policies, procedures, and teaching strategies should all align in preparing our rehearsal room for success. Yet I'm not sure we ever master classroom management (I know that I haven't). Things happen all the time that cause us to adjust our approach. Our own personality is a big factor in determining what methods of classroom management are most effective for us. We must find a way to be ourselves and still be effective. Since this book is about self-discovery, let's continue our journey by looking at policies and procedures.

## Procedures

A well-run band rehearsal is nothing more than a sequence of procedures that work in tandem to accomplish the goals of learning and music making. Let's begin with an activity that will serve as a pre-test for identifying how your rehearsals are set up.

Answer the following questions as honestly as possible. If you don't have a procedure for a particular question, simply state: "I currently do not have a procedure for this rehearsal component."

**Note:**
The following questions do not delve into the musical intent of the rehearsal. That will be handled in another chapter.

1. What is your procedure for students entering the band room before rehearsal?

St Band has playlist - music - They have 5

min to get inst. music & st.

2. What is your procedure for individual student warm-up before rehearsal begins?

3. What is your procedure for beginning class?

4.  What are the various components of your rehearsal?

    _____

    _____

    _____

    _____

5.  When you step up on the podium, is there a sense that work is to begin?

    _____

    _____

    _____

    _____

6.  What is your warm-up/fundamentals procedure and what do you wish to accomplish during this time?

    _____

    _____

    _____

    _____

7. What is your procedure for transitioning between the various components of rehearsal?

_____

_____

_____

_____

8. What is your procedure for ending rehearsal?

_____

_____

_____

_____

9. What is your procedure for dismissing rehearsal?

_____

_____

_____

_____

10. What is your procedure for students turning in written or recorded assignments?

_____

_____

_____

_____

11. What procedures are in place for students taking restroom breaks or leaving their
    seats?

_____

_____

_____

_____

12. What will be required of students if they are tardy or absent?

_____

_____

_____

_____

13. What will be required of students if the teacher is interrupted at the door or by the intercom?

_____

_____

_____

_____

14. What will be required of students if they forget their instrument and don't have it for rehearsal?

_____

_____

_____

_____

This activity is designed to make you acutely aware of the expectations that you have for your students. Most issues with classroom management can be handled with effective policies and procedures that are put in place at the beginning of the year. **Follow-through** and **consistency** are paramount in making this system work. Most students will appreciate the discipline required to make a well-run rehearsal a reality. Students yearn for structure and boundaries. The process of establishing procedures is part of the foundation that makes everything run smoothly and gives the students a sense that they have a "safe haven" *and* that you really know what you're doing. If classroom management is as critical to success as the study suggests, then effective procedures are the cornerstone to successful rehearsals.

# Code of Conduct

In addition to policies and procedures, which state **how you do what you do**, there should be a set of rules and consequences in place. Discipline plans should have clarity and state **if this, then this**. Because most schools have a discipline plan that is already enforced, band directors must decide if there will be consequences above and beyond that of the school's consequences. In some cases, this takes the form of a **Code of Conduct**, and its consequences are linked to membership or penalties within the organization. The Code of Conduct should provide parents with answers as to how you, the director, will handle situations if and when they arise.

The Code of Conduct usually addresses more severe infractions. Typical issues covered in the Code of Conduct may include:

- Drinking
- Smoking
- Any tobacco use
- Drugs
- Blatantly disobeying program rules
- Suspension
- Expulsion

List possible infractions that would be included in your discipline plan (or Code of Conduct) and the consequences for breaking program policy:

_____

_____

_____

_____

_____

_____

# Organizational Skills

Answer the following questions regarding various organizational situations within your program:

1. Do you submit paperwork and meet deadlines as requested? Name one or more occurrences in the last year when you could have "done better" in this area.

_____

_____

_____

_____

2. Are you punctual to classes and meetings? Name one or more situations in the past year where lack of punctuality got you into trouble (warranted or not).

_____

_____

_____

_____

3. Do you have an organizational framework established for staff members or booster club members that clearly articulates everyone's roles and responsibilities?

_____

_____

_____

_____

_____

4.  Do your chaperones feel informed? Name a situation in your career where lack of chaperone planning hurt you.

_____

_____

_____

_____

5.  Do you develop a Master Schedule for the entire year that is accessible to parents? Name positive and negative situations that can come out of this type of planning.

_____

_____

_____

_____

**Organizational Evaluation:**

1. Using your answers to the above questions as a guide, name your biggest organizational strengths and weaknesses in order (from weakest to strongest):

_____

_____

_____

_____

2. Are there other organizational issues that you would like to improve upon? If so, name them here: (fundraising issues, booster issues, etc.)

_____

_____

_____

_____

**Note to Self:**
In the future, I will do a better job with handling the following organizational skills...

_____

_____

_____

Basic organization is a key element in establishing a positive learning climate. This doesn't necessarily mean that your desk has to be perfect all the time, although some personality types insist upon it. (I prefer organized piles!) It does mean that you must have your "ducks in a row" and not allow slip-ups to occur just because you refuse to be organized. The job in and of itself is totally overwhelming, and some type of organizational framework must be in place for the various aspects of the program. Being organized may include:

- Having a professional and personal master schedule/calendar
- Having a filing system for bills and paperwork
- Having an organizational structure for your staff and boosters with clearly defined responsibilities
- Having a daily and weekly "To Do" list that is prioritized from most to least pressing
- Having an organized music library
- Having an organized instrument inventory
- Having an organized uniform inventory
- Having an organized rehearsal room
- Having an organized and pre-planned rehearsal/lesson plan
- Having an organized grading procedure

There is currently computer software (such as Charms) on the market to help with certain aspects of organization. One of the traits that can negatively impact effectiveness, especially with new teachers, is poor organizational skills. Take time now to evaluate your organizational effectiveness. Then go back and amend your answers to the above questions, if necessary.

## Organizing the Rehearsal

One of the most overlooked skills of the conductor is organizing and planning the rehearsal time. You should never walk out of your office with the notion that you can just "wing it" like you did yesterday. That is the least effective method of rehearsing. Answer the following questions with regard to organizing rehearsals:

1. Do you write rehearsal plans on the board? What are the advantages of doing this? Is their anything about this process that you could improve upon?

_____

_____

_____

2. Do you pre-plan a minute-by-minute timeline for how you want rehearsals to progress?

_____

_____

_____

3. Do you pre-set the seating arrangement of the ensemble prior to rehearsal time?

_____

_____

_____

4. Do you build time into your professional schedule for appropriate score study?

_____

_____

_____

5.  Do you build in time for evaluating rehearsals? This may involve listening to a recording or watching videotape of the rehearsal.

_____

_____

_____

Effective rehearsal organization is crucial to long-term success and involves much of the following:

- Selecting literature
- Establishing daily and weekly musical goals
- Organizing a daily sequence for warm-up, fundamentals, and rehearsing
- Developing a plan for pacing styles and moods within the rehearsal
- Considering equipment changes and set-up (especially percussion)
- Talking less
- Pre-planning analogies to teach various components and skills
- Planning seating arrangements
- Allotting time for score study
- Setting expectations and goals
- Evaluating rehearsals to determine a plan for future rehearsals

As we all know, rehearsals are for putting parts together—not drilling the music or facilitating skills that can be practiced at home. There are skills that students need from the conductor to ensure successful rehearsals—some musical, some not. Being aware of effective rehearsal organization and planning will set the stage for great music making.

# Chapter Checklist:

- A well-run band rehearsal is nothing more than a sequence of procedures that work in tandem to accomplish the goals of learning and music making.

- Most issues with classroom management can be handled with effective policies and procedures that are consistently implemented.

- An effective discipline plan states the consequences of a rule infraction.

- An organizational framework should be in place to handle the myriad of responsibilities involved in running a successful band program.

- Computer software (such as Charms) is an effective tool to handle typical organizational issues.

# Chapter Eight

## Professional Responsibilities

It does matter what other people think! This leads me to my one and only Frederick Fennell story.

About ten years ago, I was at the Midwest Clinic and decided just after lunch on Thursday that I was ready for a nap. I went to my room and decided that since I obviously didn't want to sleep in the suit I had been wearing, I would take one of those white robes out of the closet at the Hilton and wear it during my rest time. I put on the robe, turned on the television, and tried to get a little shut-eye. About ten minutes later, there was a knock on the door. It was the staff person who checks inventory for the wet bar refrigerator thing. She insisted she could come back, but I told her to come in so she could get her work done. As she entered the room, she pulled the metal lever into the doorway so it would allow the room door to remain open. Not thirty seconds later, there was another knock on the door. It was Frederick Fennell, and he was standing there in a tuxedo shirt and boxers—that's it! He said, "Young man, can you help me with my sleeves?" He was having trouble with his cufflinks. I said, "It would be an honor." As I stood there for what seemed like an eternity working on both sleeves, everybody and their brother walked by the room. It dawned on me that the people who were passing by (none of which I knew, thank goodness) were looking at Frederick Fennell standing just inside my room wearing boxers, I was wearing nothing but a white robe, and the wet bar maid was standing right behind both of us with a great big grin on her face.

It does matter what other people think! If it didn't matter, there would be no such thing as the job interview. There would be no need because the person with the best resume would always get the job. Since this is not the case, people skills and professional behavior are key factors to our job success and longevity.

We're all lucky that someone was willing to take a chance on us at the beginning of our careers. They obviously saw something they liked that inspired them to hire us. In this chapter, we're going to cover several issues that we, as professionals, have to face as part of the job, starting with the job interview.

# The Job Interview

For whatever reason, band director interviews are different than other job interviews. They seem to involve so much. Many times, the committee is much larger and includes parents, band students, and other important people. There seems to be so much at stake. In this section, we'll look at a few proactive steps that can be taken as part of the interview process to ensure success. We'll start with a few tips about the job interview itself.

- Present yourself in a conservative manner with appropriate attire.
- Do some research on the school, band program, and principal prior to the job interview.
- Do your homework and be prepared for the tough questions.
- Practice by doing mock interviews.
- Be prepared with a logical list of questions to ask the committee.
- Don't discuss salary, supplements, or contract until it is fairly apparent that you're going to get the job. Otherwise, let the principal bring it up.
- Come across as gracious, non-arrogant, and honest.

**Present yourself in a conservative manner with appropriate attire.**
Both men and women are expected to dress professionally. A two-piece, matched suit is always the best and safest choice. Avoid the latest fads. Also make sure everything is clean and well pressed. The key is to be conservative, from choice of clothing and color, to shoes, hairstyles, jewelry, and make-up. If you're mostly remembered for your interview attire, then you likely made an error in judgment.

**Do some research on the school, band program, and principal prior to the job interview.**
Start your research by going to both the school website and the band website. Read everything you can, including handbooks, policies and procedures, biographical information, and awards. Next, call the outgoing director and gather as much information as possible. They'll probably be intrigued to know of your interest in the position and will give you as much information as they can. Find out from the outgoing director if there are any skeletons in the closet you might need to know about. Don't base your entire opinion of the principal on the comments of the outgoing director. Just because they had issues with the principal doesn't mean you will.

**Do your homework and be prepared for the tough questions.**

Being prepared may include crafting answers for tough questions, doing mock interviews, taking along extra copies of your resume, or knowing specific issues about the program in which you're interviewing. Ask yourself: What would make me a perfect match for this job?

**Practice by doing mock interviews.**

Just as you expect students to prepare their music for rehearsal, you should prepare by doing mock interviews. The best preparation is to devise questions and role-play with a friend. The more you practice, the more calm and confident you'll be when you're actually in the hot seat. Make sure you arrive early to the interview.

**Be prepared with a logical list of questions to ask the committee.**

This is a crucial step in the interview because it conveys your interest in the job and lets the committee know you're thorough in your approach. Memorize your list so you don't have to pull out a notepad when the committee asks, "Do you have any questions for us?" Here is a short list of possible questions:

- Ask the principal about his or her philosophy for the band program.
- Ask the principal what he or she thinks is the most important role of the band.
- Ask about the number of classes currently being taught and plans for future growth and expansion.
- Ask how much rehearsal time is allotted for each ensemble.
- Ask if marching band is considered co-curricular or extracurricular.
- Ask if there is a handbook or set of policies that have already been approved and endorsed by the administration.
- Ask about current policies regarding private instruction being taught on the school premises.
- Ask about district or school financial support for the program; how funds are raised or appropriated. (Don't include your salary or supplement; just ask about the program.)

**Don't discuss salary, supplements, or contract until it is fairly apparent that you're going to get the job. Otherwise, let the principal bring it up.**

Don't discuss your individual pay scale, supplement, or benefits until you're very sure you will be offered the job (if not after you're offered the job). Giving the illusion that you're fixated on the paycheck diminishes your passion for the job and gives off an air of narrow-mindedness. Make sure your answers convey your love of teaching young people and the goals you wish to accomplish—not what you must earn to be happy.

**Come across as gracious, humble, and honest.**

This is probably the most crucial element of a successful interview. I received a phone call last week from a parent in a band booster organization who had just served on their director selection committee. He called to say that three people used me as a reference. He then proceeded to give me a play-by-play of each interview. When he got to one particular young gun, he said, "He just came across as really arrogant." Confidence is okay, but cockiness is not. Giving short, abrupt answers and giving the impression that one has done it all, seen it all, and knows everything are not virtues.

## Starting a New Job

I've had the wonderful fortune of succeeding two gifted band directors in my career. Lorraine Paris was the matriarch of band directors in our state, and she taught at the same school for 47 years. Yes, you read that correctly—47 years at the same school! She was an incredible person who single-handedly transformed a community. I also followed Miller Asbill, an amazingly talented director who laid a foundation for music making and had a charisma that made you want to follow him. We could certainly debate whether it's easier to follow someone who was successful and well liked or someone who was fired the year before. The bottom line is…most new jobs will have challenges. Students, administrators, and parents have preconceived notions of how they think the program should be run, and you may face decades of tradition. You could also face a situation where the person before you burned all bridges going out of town and really ticked some people off. Regardless of the circumstances you inherit, I think there are two basic rules that need to be at the forefront of your mind when you take over a program:

1.  *Never* say anything bad about the previous director or past performances of the band.

2.  During the first year, change as few of the things established by the previous director as possible. Only cut or adjust things you simply can't live with. There is plenty of time to make it your own.

Number two is critically important! One of the key ingredients to a successful program is developing an overall culture. The band culture should be based on excellence and should draw students to the organization. It is one of the myriad of responsibilities on a band director's "to do" list. Regardless of the previous climate, it is important to understand that you are walking into the world of adolescents or teenagers. The last thing they want to happen is for their world to be turned upside down. Transitions are tough enough as is, but for you to go into a situation and detonate a bomb simply doesn't work.

I was recently talking to a band director who was leaving after a four-year stint at a high school. The high school had been quite successful prior to his arrival, and during his tenure the program went from 158 students to 39. While there were some systemic issues, the band director admitted to me, "The biggest mistake I made was coming in and changing everything the first year. The seniors resented the changes and it went downhill from there. I so badly wanted the program to be mine that I sacrificed forty years of tradition." Also note that it's not always musical issues. One of the fundraisers that was eliminated under his watch was a supper that brought the entire town to the school once a year. Eliminating this fundraiser pulled the rug out from under the townsfolk, and consequently, the support from the town diminished greatly.

When entering a new situation, make an appointment with the outgoing director and find out as much about the program as possible (take a notepad and write everything down). It might also be helpful to meet with the current orchestra and choir director to get their perspective. For example:

- Rehearsal schedule
- Rehearsal format
- Band handbook format
- Traditional trips, contests, or concerts
- Marching or concert uniform issues
- Hiring outside staff or clinicians
- Warm-up procedures
- Private lesson procedures
- Previous literature
- Number of concerts in a given year
- Booster club organizational format
- A list of people who are important to the organization (and their roles)
- Unknown traditions
- Feeder school issues
- Traditional fundraisers
- Band banquet and graduation traditions
- Awards presented
- District and state band director association procedures and deadlines
- What's already in place for the following year

When I followed Miller Asbill, we made our appointment on the golf course. Between some rather poor shots, we talked shop. After our round, I had nine pages of notes on my yellow notepad. This process doesn't have to be painful.

After compiling all of your information, make a short list of things you absolutely cannot live with for one year. Then make a short list of things you can improve upon that are obvious to everyone (example: band handbook). Notice I said *short list*. These few items are all that need to change in the first year. If anything on your list looks particularly controversial, consider waiting to implement your new plan. Low stress during year one is crucial to success and longevity. **Remember, they don't care how much you know until they know how much you care.** After taking the first year proving that you care about them, you can slowly begin infusing new ideas into the program. After three or four years, the program will be yours and reflect your philosophy and ideals.

As for never saying anything bad about the previous director, I once heard Greg Bimm use this analogy: "It's like having two grandmothers that both make really great chocolate chip cookies. One uses Nestles chocolate chips and nuts, and the other uses Hershey's chocolate chips and no nuts. Both cookies taste great, but they each used a different approach in making them." Even if the previous director made really bad cookies, the students simply need to know that while you may do things differently, your intentions are to have an incredible band program and build on the traditions of the past. If there really were no past traditions, then you can have a discussion with your new students about developing a tradition of excellence and establishing a culture that exudes success.

# Communication

Effective communication is an essential quality for band directors. Whether you are communicating with parents, administrators, colleagues, or the general public, your public relations skills will be put to the test. In this section, we'll briefly cover communication issues typically associated with being a band director, and then you'll be asked to evaluate your effectiveness in each of these areas.

- Communicating with parents
- Communicating with administration
- Communicating with staff or other colleagues
- Communicating the virtues of the program

**Communicating with Parents:**

Technology has brought us to a point where we really have no excuse for not effectively communicating with parents. It is crucial to have an active database of parent e-mail addresses for the director and anyone else who may be involved with communication. There are also computer programs, such as "SmartMusic" that allow you to program assignment reminders into an online grade book. Three days before an assignment is due, you can send out an e-mail to both students and parents saying, "Don't forget there is an assignment due in band this Friday." Pretty cool stuff, considering the program will do it for you.

Another idea to help with communication is creating a "New Members" section for your band website, which is designed to be informative and answer any questions new students or parents might have. The new members section should include:

- A welcome letter
- Letters from students about their band experience
- Letters from parents about their band experience
- Frequently asked questions
- Common questions from students
- Common questions from parents
- Key policies within the program

From the parent perspective, it is very assuring to go to the website and read letters from other parents and students about a positive band experience.

Answer the following questions with regard to parent communication:

1. Do you effectively communicate with parents? Name one or more situations in the last year when you wished you had communicated differently with students or parents.

_____

_____

_____

_____

2. Do you have an effective handbook? Name one or more situations in the last year when having an effective handbook helped you, or when the lack of an effective handbook hindered you.

_____

_____

_____

_____

3. Do you use the internet or a newsletter as a means of communication? Name one or more situations when your band website or a newsletter helped you. Name one or more situations when having one or the other *could* have helped you.

_____

_____

_____

_____

**Communicating with Administration:**

Before discussing the act of communicating with your administration, I would like to share my personal thoughts: They don't care how much you know…until you demonstrate integrity and the ability to be a team player. There really is a bit of pre-work that needs to be done before a new boss or administrator will be willing to establish two-way communication. Otherwise, you will get the reputation of only going to the boss when *you* need something. I honestly believe you cannot effectively communicate with your boss or any other significant person if you haven't laid some type of foundational trust. Personal character, professionalism, imagination, and the ability to turn water into wine are all characteristics that are necessary in establishing a great relationship with your principal or dean. Don't expect your administration to be accepting with open arms if you have a reputation of saying inappropriate things to students or not being a team player. Don't misunderstand—I'm not saying you have to be a "kiss up" to get your administrator to listen. You do, however, have to maintain a certain amount of trustworthiness and moral character. All bosses want to have a sense that you are trying to be the best "you" that you can be. In today's society, most corporate heads are not seeking "yes" people; they want a team of people with many types of ideas, styles, personalities, and skill sets. If you are attempting to be the best director that you can be, it is a much easier sell when you approach your administrator. Some folks are busting it at their jobs, but they forget the integrity piece with regards to perceptions from their boss.

I've been involved in several situations when people have called in a crisis and asked for advice on talking to their administrator. In most cases, what I ultimately find in the conversation is that the communication bridge has already been blown to shreds. At that point, the recommended solution is to pick up the pieces, heal the wounds, and rescue what little can be salvaged.

To establish a healthy line of communication with your administration, do the pre-work first: be a great team player and be really good at what you do! Also be aware that there are several areas in which you need your boss on your side, including:

- Scheduling
- Philosophy of the program
- What classes to teach
- Hiring additional staff
- Enforcing policies and procedures
- Discipline plans
- Booster by-laws
- Specific issues within the overall school climate

The list could be endless (although let's hope not). Achieving and getting results from this relationship requires you to be prepared with good, solid answers and information. I find that when I want to make a passionate argument, I have to prepare as if it were a court case. My rationale better be logical, have substance, and have some source of information to support it.

One of my colleagues is a middle school director. His principal decided to change their schedule from a traditional seven-period day to an A/B day block. This meant he would go from seeing his students every day to seeing them every other day. He felt very passionately that he would rather see them every day for some logical amount of time than to see them every other day. His initial logic was based on the fact that there would be some weeks when he would see them only twice. And what if one of the students forgot his or her instrument because he or she confused the A/B days? Or what if there was testing on some days? Or what if they decided to have an assembly program on one of the class days? However, the tipping point came when he began to do some research and determined that there was tangible evidence to suggest that for the performing arts, consistent, everyday instruction was proven to be more beneficial to students. He presented the mountain of evidence to his principal, and the decision to initiate the A/B day schedule was reversed. They opted for a modified block, which allowed performing arts students to attend class every day. Doing his homework was a huge payoff.

Answer the following questions with regard to your administration:

1.  Does your administration perceive you as being professional, a team player, and full of integrity?

    _____

    _____

    _____

2.  Name one or more situations when your reputation helped you, or when your reputation hindered you.

    _____

    _____

    _____

3.  Are you considered "high maintenance" by other members of the faculty or administration?

    _____

    _____

    _____

**Communicating with Staff and Other Colleagues:**

I recently hired a new member of our band staff and was somewhat surprised at one of his initial comments. He said, "The other staff members tell me that you like to lay everything out on the table, and if we disagree, that it's okay." I told him that his information was correct and that I was certainly not looking for "yes" people to make up our staff. I went on to explain that I hire people who have their own individual strengths and that each member of the team possesses several unique qualities and skills that make them a valuable member. That's why I hired him. He smiled.

My experience has been that the worst scenario within a band program (or school of music) is the perception that everything is just peachy when, in reality, staff members are talking behind each other's backs about how they think things should be run. This issue can literally bring a band program to its knees and is totally unhealthy. The same is also true if the band staff does not agree on the philosophy by which the program will be run. One staff member can literally be a cancer to the entire operation and, ultimately, it will rear its ugly head! The person who must codify all of these issues into one harmonious plan is the director. This does not mean that the best approach is always "my way or the highway." Sometimes this is a necessary approach, but a better way of conducting business is for everyone to feel as if they have a voice and are a vital member of the team. Effective communication among staff members and ground rules for how to communicate are vital to the health of the organization. As the leader, it is important to listen to others as a means of getting everyone on the same page. Who knows? You might learn something in the process.

The following proactive steps are recommended to foster effective communication with and between staff members and colleagues:

- Devise a clear outline of duties and responsibilities; make sure to include your own jobs so it doesn't appear as though they are your new dumping ground.
- Effectively communicate expectations for everyone on the staff.
- Have a plan for running efficient staff meetings.
- Have a plan for running efficient rehearsals.
- Have a method for setting goals.
- Have a method for grading and instruction.
- Have a cohesive method for effective assessment.
- Have a plan for resolving discourse and voicing concerns.
- Have some type of leadership development so each member of the team is contributing to his or her fullest potential.

There are four books I would like to recommend that address work-related communication and leadership training:

1.  *The Five Dysfunctions of a Team* by Patrick Lencioni (Jossey-Bass, 2002)
2.  *Death by Meeting* by Patrick Lencioni (Jossey-Bass, 2004)
3.  *The Four Obsessions of an Extraordinary Executive* by Patrick Lencioni (Jossey-Bass, 2000)
4.  *QBQ! The Question Behind the Question* (Putnam Publishing, 2004)

Whether you view it this way or not, you are the executive in charge of making everyone sing—harmoniously.

Answer the following questions with regard to staff and other colleagues:

1.  Do the folks who work with your students know (and are aware of) the philosophy of the program?

_____

_____

_____

_____

2.  Have you established ground rules for effective communication within your organization, and are those steps followed during staff meetings?

_____

_____

_____

_____

3. Have you provided a clear list of duties and responsibilities for each member of the team?

_____

_____

_____

_____

**Communicating the Virtues of the Program:**

One of the noblest responsibilities we have as directors is communicating the virtues of our program. It should be easy to get excited about our jobs if we reconnect with those feelings that brought us into the profession in the first place. Sometimes it's easy to get caught up in the day-to-day grind and forget why we believe so passionately in what we do. In terms of communicating these ideals, it is important to realize that everyone doesn't see what we do through the same colored glasses. This is why it is so important to continually sing the praises of music education and what it can do for young people. It is more than advocacy, although a strong advocacy campaign is important. It is about transforming lives through the medium of music. Our administration may see things more from the perspective of what the band does for the overall school climate. Parents may see band as a way for their child to spend quality time with other students their own age. Community members may see the program as being great ambassadors for the town. All of these things are certainly true, but the number one reason we do what we do is to cultivate a love and passion for music and music making. Through this process, we also get to instill some incredible life lessons and skills, which put us in the category of being in the "people" business. There is nothing more noble, in my opinion. Being in the people business is teaching to the future, which means we serve as mentors for life.

There are several ways to effectively communicate the virtues of what we do. First, there is an enormous amount of research to back up the positive values of the study of the arts. *Arts with the Brain in Mind* by Eric Jenson (ASCD Premium Member book, 2001) is a great resource from the mental development perspective. Conn-Selmer has devoted a great deal of resources toward arts advocacy and its benefits. NAMM, Music for All, and MENC are all strong resources and incredible advocates for the arts.

Following is a list of some of the benefits we can share with our constituents:

- The study of music and music making
- Leadership training
- Developing a culture of positive life skills
- Producing great thinkers and cultivating creativity and self-expression
- Contributing positively to school life
- Creating a safe haven for young people
- Producing a sense of belonging within its members
- Developing individual responsibility

What are some of the other student benefits of belonging to your program?

_____

_____

_____

_____

One of my former student teachers recently asked if he could schedule a meeting with me. He is an incredible young man with saintly integrity. He was very clear with me from the beginning of his student teaching experience that he wanted to teach in a low-income neighborhood and help kids who couldn't help themselves. He is currently the band director at a very poor, underprivileged school. He inherited the program in mid-year and is doing an incredible job. After we got past the small talk, he said, "I know that our biggest responsibility is to develop each student to his or her full musical potential. I don't think that I'm doing that. What should I do?" I asked him to give me more background about his program. He went on to say with a great deal of pride that when he inherited the program, he had six students. Over the course of the semester, more and more students came to him and asked if they could join the band program. For next year, he has 54 students enrolled in band, and 48 of them are beginners or have had less than six months of instruction. I asked him why he thought he was having such success recruiting. His response was, " I think that I have provided a place for them to belong. The band room has turned into a safe haven, and many students come there just to hang out." If it's easy to get excited about being in the people business, this young man should be on cloud nine. He has planted the seeds for developing a culture of excellence. He may be the only beacon of light in these young people's lives. We spent the remainder of our conversation on the "developing a culture" component and set very small musical goals. I encouraged him to evaluate his situation based on progress only, and I gave him the phone number of another band director who took a similar situation along the same path, who has changed a community over the past 14 years and has slowly developed musical excellence. When he arrived fourteen years ago, the band was playing grade 1.5 music. Today, they are playing grade 5 literature at festival with exceptional music making skills. In addition, his students are some of the finest, most polite young men and women I've been around.

Although each of these directors are in two distinctly different situations (one rural and the other low socio-economic), both of them are changing the lives of young people in the most profound way.

Answer the following questions with regard to the virtues of your program:

1. How might communicating the virtues of the program help with recruitment and retention?

_____

_____

_____

_____

2. Name a situation when communicating the virtues of the program served as a huge benefit to you and your students.

_____

_____

_____

_____

3. Name a crisis situation when being armed with effective advocacy information could help the program.

_____

_____

_____

_____

## Chapter Checklist:

- Prepare and practice prior to taking a job interview.

- When starting a new job, never say anything bad about the previous director, and change as little as possible during the first year.

- Effective communication is an essential quality of a successful band director and should be a high priority when entering a new teaching situation.

- Devise a clear outline of duties for everyone on your staff, including yourself.

- Effectively communicating the virtues of the program is a vital part of recruitment and should lead to program growth.

Philosophy –
responsibility to our students

The next morning the boys set out just as planned, captured a young bird, and started the trek up the mountain to the old man's cabin. When they arrived, one boy knocked on the door while the other held the bird. As the door opened, they noticed an elderly gentleman with sand-white hair and deep blue eyes. One of the boys said to the old man: "O wise one, can you tell me what I hold in my hand?" The wise man stated, "Based on the chirping and fluttering, my guess is that you hold a bird in your hand." The young men were very impressed and said, "You are indeed a wise man. Now tell us, old wise one, is the bird that I hold in my hand dead or alive?" The wise man took several minutes to answer because he knew that if he said "alive," they would squeeze the bird to death. If he said "dead," they would let the bird go and he would be wrong either way. Finally, the wise man raised his head and peered with those deep blue eyes into the souls of the young men and said, "The bird's fate is as you will it."

The lesson here is that, indeed, **the band's fate is…as you will it.** The band's fate is in your hands. What powerful words to offer in helping us understand that a good plan and patience will enable us to achieve any goal, but we must "will it" before it can actually come to fruition. Most things we label as "problems" can be solved by looking in the mirror. A written plan that promotes growth, sets goals, and provides a snapshot of the future is what creating a professional mission statement is all about.

I like to call this process creating the perfect scenario. Attorney Shirley Hufstedler stated, "You have to be able to envision in fairly concrete terms what ought to be done or what you want to do or where you want to go… A certain amount of conceptualization is required. It's not unlike planning for a trip." Some people may call it dreaming, meditating, or goal setting, but regardless of its title, this is the initial process in writing your professional mission statement. Begin by making a list of your personal goals as they relate to your band program. Remember to dream big, but be realistic about what is actually attainable. If you accept a job at a small high school that has been struggling for several years, set your goals accordingly. Many small successes at the beginning will go a long way in believing in the power of a written plan.

Answer the following questions with a brief belief statement. Make sure your statements are significant and get to the very heart of why you are a band director. Your statements should include values you wish to instill in your students—musical or otherwise. For example, your first statement might be:

To use the medium of music to teach life lessons, to provide life-changing experiences, to build bonds, and to create something musically significant.

This could be the "professional" statement that gives you a solid foundation for the remainder of your mission statement.

1.  Why does your band program exist?

_____

_____

_____

_____

2.  What "lessons of life" do you want to instill in your students?

_____

_____

_____

_____

3.  What musical concepts do you want to provide for your students?

― appreciaton_____

_____

_____

_____

4.  What will make your band program unique or recognizable?

_____

_____

_____

_____

5.  What do you plan to achieve in two years, five years, and ten years?

_____

_____

_____

_____

6.  When you hire other staff members, what should their most important qualities be?

_____

_____

_____

_____

7. If you could clearly communicate one message to your students, what would it be? (Try to keep this to a one-sentence response.)

_____

_____

_____

_____

Also respond to the following statements:

Name one or several things you are currently *not* doing that you would like to implement next school year within the band program. My goals for the program are:

_____

_____

_____

_____

Name things that need to be changed within your band program:

_____

_____

_____

_____

From reading this book, I have a new sense of...

_____

_____

_____

_____

As a band director, my greatest goals are...

_____

_____

_____

_____

You are now ready to begin the first draft of your professional mission statement. For this exercise, begin by rewriting your five most important sentences (or thoughts) from the exercise above in bulleted form:

1. _____

2. _____

3. _____

4. _____

5. _____

Additional sentences:

_____

_____

_____

_____

**Helpful hint:**

If this system is not what you prefer, close the book and begin your own format (version) of your professional mission statement. When you're done, ask yourself if this written plan represents your feelings, goals, and aspirations. You may want to assign a heading to each section of the document. For example: (a) Short-term Goals, (b) Long-term Goals, (c) Personal Goals, (d) Other Goals.

# My Professional Mission Statement
## *FULL DRAFT*

The reason for education is to serve each students right to benefit clearly and valuably by instruction. My responsibility is to provide for the musical needs of all students. It is not nearly enough to create a good secondary music program, it is about what the program does to enhance the musical understanding for individual students & what I do to respond to the influence of the changing world of music in a quickly growing society.

# Affirming the Plan

Earlier in the book I referenced Dave Ramsey. I was listening one day to his financial show on talk radio. The caller asked if he should borrow money from his 401-K to pay off his credit cards. Dave was quick to point out that if the only consideration were interest rate, then it would be a good move. However, he went on to say that he would definitely not recommend the concept of borrowing from oneself to pay off debt because of the fundamental concept that you haven't changed the behavior that caused the debt in the first place. Most folks who take the easy way out of paying off debt find themselves in the same mess a year down the road because they haven't made a paradigm shift in the way they handle their finances.

Band directors are sometimes the same. They have the right intentions, but they don't change what they have always done. Consequently, they stay in the same rut and exhibit the same patterns. Writing your professional mission statement is not enough. You must believe that effective change will yield results. One of the ways to begin the paradigm shift necessary for success is to affirm your plan. Your words and your goals must be aligned.

Now that you have written the first draft of your professional mission statement, it is time to move to the next step in the process, which involves rewriting your plan in the "here and now." Restate the sentences as if they are happening in the moment.

**Example:**
I would like to attain a level of performance that deserves a Superior rating at concert festival.

**In the "here and now":**
We have now attained a level of performance that deserves a Superior rating at concert festival.

I am not one of those people who believes that if you recite your wants and desires one hundred times before you go to bed they will come true in the morning. I do believe, however, that you must have a plan for improvement and you must have the correct *attitude* to get there. This practice of affirmation is actually an ancient Hindu custom, but it is as relevant today as it was eleven hundred years ago. If you can state your career mission as something that is active (as opposed to "somewhere out there"), it will become a part of who you are. Most of our habits, quirks, and mannerisms were developed in much the same way.

Take the five key statements of your mission statement and write them in the "here and now."

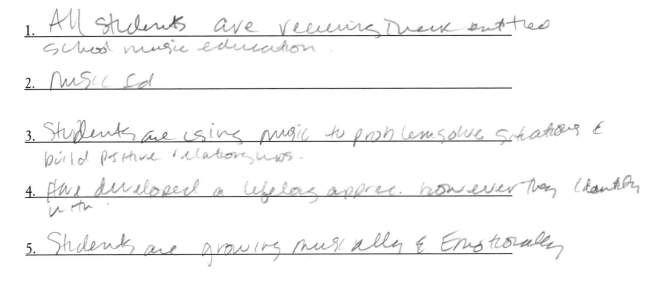

1. All students are receiving their entitled school music education.

2. Music Ed

3. Students are using music to problemsolve situations & build positive relationships.

4. Have developed a lifelong apprec. however they change in the.

5. Students are growing musically & Emotionally

## Implementing the Plan

Once you have stated your professional mission statement components as active affirmations, it is time to go to the next step. This step involves stating **how you will arrive at the "here and now,"** or to put it another way, what strategies you must use to make these dreams into realities—not how you teach a component, but *how you reach a goal.* If a seventeen-year-old decides he or she wants to become a teacher but is not willing to go to college to receive the training necessary for certification, the dream will simply not become a reality. Professional mission statements are inanimate in much the same way. You must develop a plan that yields results, or the mission statement is essentially useless. Implementing the plan is a way to jumpstart the professional mission statement and say, "Now that I have a statement that holds me accountable, what must I do to get the ball rolling?"

Because this workbook is designed to help you find solutions, you will answer a series of questions that will help yield key results. Before we get started, here is an example:

If part of your professional mission statement is to **develop great players,** then your answers could be the following:

1. Hire private instructors.
2. Teach private lessons myself.
3. Motivate the students to practice by providing incentives.
4. Use the **Phrasing** and **Musicianship** bullets to develop musical awareness.

Notice that this falls within the realm of what you can do to help achieve the goal. Take the time now to complete the following exercise and devise a personal plan for implementing your professional mission statement.

List the **first** sentence of your professional mission statement as a goal:

Develop life long appreciation of music in whatever form students identify with

Name three things you can personally do to make this goal a reality:

1. present many genres of music

2. put aside my personal feelings about student music interest

3.

List the **second** statement as a goal:

Name three things you can personally do to make this goal a reality:

1.

2.

3.

List the **third** statement as a goal:

_____

_____

_____

Name three things you can personally do to make this goal a reality:

1. _____

2. _____

3. _____

List the **fourth** statement as a goal:

_____

_____

_____

Name three things you can personally do to make this goal a reality:

1. _____

2. _____

3. _____

List the **fifth** statement as a goal:

_____

_____

_____

Name three things you can personally do to make this goal a reality:

1. _____

2. _____

3. _____

Continue this process for your entire professional mission statement. Some of your answers may overlap. You have probably already figured out that this requires a great deal of hard work to reinvent yourself and turn your desires into reality. Another thing you might have discovered in this process is that some of your goals originally written in the professional mission statement are either "fluff" (I would like to give everyone in the world a puppy) or simply not attainable (I just want everyone to get along). If this is the case, revise your professional mission statement to reflect substantive goals with logical outcomes.

To finish the chapter, write a journal entry that states the following:

For the band program to get better, I must...

_____

_____

_____

_____

_____

_____

_____

_____

_____

_____

_____

_____

## Chapter Checklist:

- A professional mission statement should contain a list of goals, dreams, and aspirations for both you and the program.

- A professional mission statement should get to the essence of what you want to instill into the program and have music making as a basic core belief.

- You must devise action strategies for accomplishing your goals and objectives contained in the professional mission statement.

# Chapter Ten

# Ten Leadership Questions

Getting tangible results from the student leadership process is an elusive endeavor, but we would all love for this aspect of the program to be thriving. Our hope is that students will take personal ownership in their behavior, conduct, musical product, and willingness to contribute to something significant.

In this chapter, we'll examine several leadership truths that are absolutes, regardless of your leadership style or how active you'd like your student leaders to be. All groups have leaders; the goal is to establish a core message for your program and train your student leaders to be a reflection of those core values and beliefs.

Each year, I ask potential leadership candidates to write a paper telling me why they should be considered for leadership and why they would make a great candidate. The best leadership paper I've ever received went like this:

Leadership is nothing more than me being the best "me" that I can be, while attempting to continuously do the right thing.

— Jenny

That was it. No eloquent dissertation or "Webster's defines leadership as..." Plain and simple—Jenny got it! I didn't have to worry about whether she was a good choice.

Just yesterday, another of my students came in the office and said:

How can I best serve the band? I want to be in a position to make the most impact.

— Sarah

Sarah also got it! My response to Sarah was, "Can I clone you?" If life were always this easy, it would be grand, wouldn't it? The truth is that leadership is a process that has no real destination. Leadership training is about establishing a culture in your band program that aligns with your core values and philosophy. Scott Lang says you must state your core value beliefs 21 consecutive days for it to make an impact on your students. My core value belief is:

**The kind of person you are
is more important than the musician you become!**

For the music purist, there is no conflict of interest here. If you're the best person you can be, then you'll want to be the best musician you can be. The statement is a core value belief, and it is the type of foundation on which great programs are built. As one of my colleagues used to say, "You've got to stand for something, so it might as well be something positive."

The ability to have influence on someone must begin with your willingness to establish a relationship with them first: **They don't care how much you know until they know how much you care!** This is the precursor to developing a culture of leadership in your program. After proving that you care about them, you can then instill core values into the process. This is also true for your student leaders.

If you could summarize your core belief in one sentence or less, what would it be?

_Be a good Human - Be kind, Be_

_helpful & Be aware_

## The Ten Questions

Now that you've established a premise on which to run your program, answer the following questions. Expound on each answer to include reactions about your program:

1.  Are the student leaders developing a relationship with the followers and teaching with the heart of a teacher?

2. Do the student leaders "practice what they preach," or are they hypocrites?

_____

_____

3. What strengths will individual student leaders bring to the leadership group? What qualities must they have to be effective in the leadership group?

_____

_____

4. Do the student leaders praise when they see the followers doing good things, or are they simply turning into questionable leaders who only seem to notice bad behaviors?

_____

_____

5. Are your student leaders willing to give more to save them than the bullies (negative leaders) are to take them away (to another activity or behavior)?

_____

_____

6. Do the student leaders try to involve or include negative leaders and make this relationship a positive one, or do they simply seek to ostracize and cast out the bad apples?

_____

_____

7.  Can the student leaders answer the question, "What specific things have I done to serve the members of my section, the band, the organization?"

_____

_____

8.  What can the student leaders do to make your life as a band director more efficient?

_____

_____

9.  Have the student leaders been trained to develop momentum for the group and to create a culture of excellence?

_____

_____

10. Do you send the student leaders out to "just lead," or do they have a mission, vision, purpose, and goals?

_____

_____

# The Five Principles

**Principle #1: Student leaders must lead by example.**

Group dynamics dictate that if you want an ensemble to develop chemistry and a sense of momentum, the leaders (including the adults) must be wonderful examples and role models. Young people are yearning for great role models, even amongst their peers. You can ask students in your program who they think are great role models, and they will tell you.

During our drum major interviews, I ask candidates if they have role models. In virtually every case, one of several role models will be someone in the band program who they feel is a great person. Sometimes it's a former student leader who made an impact on their lives. Great student leaders walk their talk; they're the same person in the group as they are outside of the group. Great student leaders also understand that one of their roles is to create momentum in the group.

The best way to start good habits and practices are for the leaders to get it right and take ten more students by the hand and lead them along this journey called "building a tradition." If the leaders are truly leading by example, even the negative leaders will reluctantly move forward with the group.

**Principle #2: Student leaders must have integrity and believability.**
This may be the most important attribute of an effective student leader. The reason is the concept of adolescent students leading other adolescent students is a tough game from the outset. Students will follow someone with integrity who they trust, who is consistent in every situation, and who is not a hypocrite. Student leaders with integrity follow through on their commitments and promises. The most common complaint is, "She's always telling me to stop talking, but she talks more than anyone in the section."

As the director, it is important to truly have your finger on the pulse of which students truly have believability. It's better to pick fewer student leaders with high moral standards and character than to sprinkle a few marginal leaders into the mix.

**Principle #3: Student leaders must develop a culture.**
Wow! This one's tough because it's a huge responsibility for student leaders. Developing a culture says, "This is how we do things around here." It's more than leading by example because it causes student leaders to have vision and be major players in the dynamics of group ownership. The more they give, the more the group will grow. You can have a great group of students who lead by example, but if the negative leaders are creating the culture, you're doomed.

Creating a culture means the environment is so exciting and dynamic that no one would want to leave the group. It means the program is a place where students have a sense of belonging. Developing a culture means the group stands for something extraordinary, and the feelings the members get from belonging can't be duplicated anywhere else. Personal integrity and group cohesiveness are cornerstones to building and developing a culture.

**Principle #4: Student leaders must be willing to work hard and realize that their role is a position of service.**
This sounds simple enough, but it's one of the hardest character traits to develop. Young people, by nature, are only willing to take this idea to a point. Student leaders need a lot of help and guidance to facilitate just what they're capable of achieving if they lead from the bottom up. Young people are resourceful, creative, and intelligent, and your job as director is to widen their scope of influence and provide direction.

Taking on the workload means student leaders can help you, serve individuals in their section, and think of ideas outside of the box. It also means they can tighten music stands, load equipment, and do the dirty clean- up work. Student leaders are there to serve others—and it's usually a thankless job.

**Principle #5: Student leaders must have a vision, mission, and purpose.**
The biggest mistake directors make in the leadership journey is asking students to lead and then not equipping them to do so. Students need direction, training, and a purpose. The leadership group needs to write a mission statement and then develop "buy-in" from the remainder of the group. Just as the head director should clearly communicate roles and responsibilities to other staff members, you need to do the same for your leadership team. Don't send your leaders into the lion's den (the rest of the band) and say, "Fend for yourselves." They will come back wounded and beat up. I know, because I've done it! Students need to know how to handle each leadership scenario; much time must be devoted to the training of effective leaders.

To be an effective leader, you not only have to get the group of followers on your side, but you must also be able to convince them that whatever obstacle stands in the way, there's a solution for it (which usually involves hard work). All life journeys require negotiating your way through obstacles, and followers want to know that there are people they can count on to get them through the tough situations.

Answer the following questions regarding your leadership team:

What is the purpose of your leadership team?

_____

_____

What changes need to be made to your leadership team from past years and experiences?

_____

_____

What specific training do your leaders need compared to what's been offered in the past?

_____

_____

What things do you expect your student leaders to do without being asked?

_____

_____

What things do you consider outside of their realm of influence—things you don't want them to handle?

_____

_____

Based on Principle #5, these are all issues that need to be clearly communicated to your student leaders. Maybe even more rewarding would be to pose these questions to your student leaders and hear how they answer them. It's a great catalyst for leadership training.

## Integrity Plus Discipline Equals Success

Program and personal integrity is paramount to success if you truly believe that you're in the people business. Students must have a moral compass and believe that character is a valuable attribute. Earlier, I mentioned that a core belief for me was:

**The kind of person you are**
**is more important than the musician you become.**

I also believe:

**Integrity plus discipline equals success.**

I think every band program should have such credos as a normal part of the everyday curriculum. When Scott Lang was a director, he had three axioms his band lived by. They were: (1) discipline before instruction, (2) behavior before performance, and (3) we are better only if we work harder. What a clear vision and purpose for a program.

Take time now to write three axioms you believe to be core beliefs within your program. (If you'd like, you can use the one you wrote earlier as number one.) After writing and revising your axioms, present them to your leadership group for their input. After working on them together, display your finished product in the band room for the entire group to see.

Core Belief #1

_Beleve in yourself -_

_- Be the best you can be_

Core: Belief #2

_Be a good human - Be kind, Be Helpful_

_Be a uape_

Core Belief #3

_Responsible Music live - are a music team_

# Chapter Checklist:

- Students must know that both the director and student leaders care about them before they will truly buy into any belief system.

- Establish a belief system that permeates the program to develop a culture and tradition of excellence.

- Student leaders must have integrity and believability.

- Leadership students must take ownership by first leading by example.

- Other than leading by example, student leaders must be willing to work.

- Leadership students must have a purpose and a mission.

# For college students only:

- Would I be considered an excellent student leader in my college/ university music program?

- Do I come across to my colleagues as mature and ready to enter the teaching profession?

- Do I practice my instrument to the degree that I can pass on a musical legacy to my students?

- Am I a positive force in creating a culture and tradition of excellence in this institution's program?

- Am I a person of integrity?

- Am I leading by example?

- Do I exhibit positive leadership and a level of musical excellence by diligently practicing my part outside of rehearsal?

- Am I willing to step in and help without anyone asking?

- If I am unwilling to develop leadership qualities in myself, should I expect these qualities from my future student leaders?

- Would I be comfortable asking any of my college professors to write a strong letter of recommendation for a teaching position based on my ability to lead?

# Chapter Eleven

# What's Really Important in Life

We've spent a great deal of time working on your professional life. At minimum, you should be armed with a few true gems of wisdom you can apply to your teaching experience. If you've really searched for answers, this process should have yielded many epiphany moments that have invigorated you and made you think, "I can't wait to try this stuff!" You should also have a written plan in place that will guide you from this point forward to allow you to set, meet, and exceed your goals. But what happens if you've climbed the ladder of success, only to realize that it's against the wrong wall?

## Bruce

My brother passed away a few years back. Bruce was an amazing person. Fifteen hundred people showed up for the family visitation, which was real evidence of what I knew all along, that Bruce had literally touched the lives of thousands of people. Why does it take something so jarring—so permanent—to refocus our efforts on what is really important? I'm sure you have stories and people in your life that keep you well grounded in what's truly important in life.

Bruce was President and CEO of Leroy Springs and Company, a philanthropic subsidiary of Springs Industries, the company that makes Springmaid sheets, towels, and many of the things we have in our homes. The part of the company Bruce headed was established to take care of the employees of Springs and to make significant contributions to the communities in which they worked. Bruce was a people person, and his work was certainly people-centered. He was always associated with a funny story, and he himself was a magnificent storyteller. Even if you had heard one of his stories before, you would still listen because he would always embellish it and make it more sensational the next time around. Bruce made people laugh, and as a business-man, he had a way of getting what he wanted out of people without them knowing that he had an intent and purpose behind everything he asked them to do. He was an incredible brother who died at the age of 56 due to complications after surgery to remove cancer. Like many great people, he died way too early and had much more to contribute to this world. Bruce taught me that you could have a passion for your work and be really excited about being in the people business. Bruce knew how to keep it in perspective.

## Thomas

Talk about something that helps keep it all in perspective...Thomas is my one and only child. My wife Michelle and I plan everything, and Thomas was no exception. Thomas was a very cooperative infant, so it was not unusual to us that he came at exactly the right time (okay, one day early) and was birthed in a record twenty-two minutes. Thomas is the joy of my life, and everything else revolves around making sure that a band director's schedule does not overtake time with Thomas. It has literally been the toughest and most rewarding thing about our marriage, and we are both continually making decisions on his behalf. The toughest thing for me is that I believe that being a musician/teacher is a *calling*; it's what I was put here to do. I believe my contribution to the world is what I'm giving through my vocation, and it's what I love to do. With that said, my greatest responsibility in the entire world is being a great parent to Thomas! Thomas knows that we love him, love each other, and will provide for his needs. As the saying goes, "Nobody ever said on their deathbed, I wish I would have spent more time at the band room." Our priority should be to constantly find ways to be effective but yet keep the job in perspective. Thomas has taught me that work can wait, especially since the years are flying by.

## Randy Pausch

Many of you know the story of Randy Pausch, the professor at Carnegie-Mellon University who was diagnosed with pancreatic cancer. Randy, who had a wonderful wife, Jai, and three children, was informed that he had three months to live, and he chose to live it with the most amazing sense of dignity and purpose. He died on July 25, 2008. On the college campus of Carnegie-Mellon, professors are asked to give a lecture entitled "The Last Lecture," in which they present their life's work. Randy was asked to present his "last lecture," and it was, profoundly, his last. Randy's "last lecture" was attended by scores of people and had very, very little to do with academia. His moment of sharing was intended to leave a legacy and establish a message by which his own children could grow up knowing the things their father felt were really important. I strongly recommend the book *The Last Lecture* (Hyperion, 2008) and hope you will put it in your library. You can also hear his entire "last lecture" online.

Well, what does this all mean? I have spent a lot of time trying to determine how these experiences have affected me personally and how they have permeated my professional life. I suppose the overwhelming sentiment is that we should live every day to affect others in some profound way and, more than anything else, we should treasure our dearest relationships. Professionally, we get to use the vehicle of music to touch lives and provide meaningful moments for our students, and this should never be taken for granted. Personally, it's the people closest to us that should mean the most.

In the end, I want to give my students a passion for music and music making, and a true sense of who they are. This can take the form of an honest realization about whether they're really giving it their best shot or just a sense of their own integrity and character. I want them to bring out the best in others and leave a legacy.

My wish for you is that when you get in the car in the morning, you feel thankful and blessed to have a vocation that uses music to both communicate and change lives. I also hope you treasure the most important people in your life and never take them for granted.

Well, we've gotten to the end of our journey. I hope that through this process of self-discovery, you have a true sense of who you are and who you need to be. This is not in any way an ending, but the beginning of implementing your plan of action!

## Final Project

If you had to give your "Last Lecture," what would you say?

_____

_____

_____

_____

_____

I want to leave you with this quote from *Self-Renewal: The Individual and the Innovative Society* (W. W. Norton and Co., 1996) by John Gardner.

Exploration of the full range of our own potentialities is not something that we can safely leave to the chances in life. It is something to be pursued systematically, or at least avidly, to the end of our days.

# Acknowledgments

Proverbs 3:5–6

To my amazing wife, Michelle, for her unconditional love.

To my wonderful son, Thomas, for teaching me what's really important in life.

To my parents and siblings, for being such great examples.

To my students, for allowing me to be a part of their lives
and for the opportunity to make music together.

To my teaching colleagues:
Sean McGrew, Lanie Radecke, Jeff Scott, Nick Nafpliotis,
Marie Evans, Michael Gray, Tim Cole, Bobby Bethea, and Jessica Crum.

To Gary Gribble, Rebecca Phillips, and Kevin Geraldi,
for your feedback on this project.

A very special thanks to Jay Gilbert, for all of your invaluable help
and for the incredible gift and contribution of the Study Guide.

To Rod Winther, Frank Battisti, and Gary Green,
for your wonderful support and kind words.

To Robert Wertz, Pat Wylie, James Copenhaver, and Frank Battisti,
for your gift to inspire.

To Robert Pruzin and Charles Kavalovski, for teaching me how to teach and
perform, and for providing the true definition of being a professional.

To Tim Lautzenheiser, for your inspiration and encouragement.

To Alec Harris, Linda Vickers, and all the folks at GIA Publications,
for your unending dedication to music education.

# Appendix A
## The Four T's Assessment Model

The Four T's Assessment Model focuses on each of these four key components. Devise exercises, studies, and written assignments to evaluate mastery of each. Appropriate assessment should yield the best results within your teaching situation and level.

I can assess *Timing* by:

_____

_____

_____

_____

I can assess *Tuning* by:

_____

_____

_____

_____

I can assess *Tone* by:

_____

_____

_____

_____

I can assess *Technique* by:

_____

_____

_____

_____

# Appendix B
## The Three-Tiered Assessment Model

**Master Musician:**

- Two contrasting movements from a major solo work written for your instrument
- All twelve major scales and the three forms of minor in the following keys: Bb, F, C, G, D, A, and E
- Key recognition test for Majors, minors, and identification of relative Major/minors
- Sight-reading through difficult mixed meter
- Sight-singing a difficult solfege passage

**Advanced Musician:**

- One complete movement of a concerto or sonata
- All twelve major scales for the full range of the instrument
- Key recognition test for all major scales
- Sight-reading at Senior All-State level
- Sight-singing a moderate solfege passage

**Intermediate Musician:**

- An All-State etude or any approved solo, grade III or higher
- Nine scales in the following keys: Bb, Eb, Ab, Db, G, C, F, D, and A
- Key signature test of major scales
- Sight-reading at Grade 9–10 All-State level
- Sight-singing an easy solfege passage

### Maximum Grading Scale

| Symphonic Band: | | | |
|---|---|---|---|
| | 100 | = | Master Musician |
| | 95 | = | Advanced Musician |
| | 90 | = | Intermediate Musician |

| **Concert Band:** | 100+ | = | Master Musician |
| | 100 | = | Advanced Musician |
| | 95 | = | Intermediate Musician |
| | | | |
| **Chamber Winds:** | 100+ | = | Advanced Musician |
| | 95+ | = | Intermediate Musician |

If a student chooses to mix and match levels for a grade, a weighted formula has been devised to determine the appropriate grade.

# Appendix C
## Individual Performance Rubric

**Directions:**

The total score for a criterion is calculated by multiplying the weight for the criterion by the score. The total score for each criterion is summed to produce the total performance score.

## Individual Performance Rubric

*devised and created by Scott Rush and Dr. Christina Schneider*

| Criteria | Scale | | | | | Weight | Total Score |
|---|---|---|---|---|---|---|---|
| | 1 | 2 | 3 | 4 | 5 | | |
| Pitches | Pitches performed inaccurately and mistakes detract from many areas of the performance | Pitches performed somewhat accurately and mistakes detract from some areas of the performance | Most pitches performed accurately and mistakes do not severely detract from the performance | All pitches performed accurately | | 3.5 | |
| Rhythms | Rhythms performed inaccurately and mistakes detract from many areas of the performance | Rhythms performed somewhat accurately and mistakes detract from some areas of the performance | Most rhythms performed accurately and mistakes do not severely detract from the performance | All rhythms performed accurately | | 3.5 | |
| Timing (steady pulse) | A consistent underlying pulse is not present throughout the performance, which severely detracts from the performance | A consistent underlying pulse is not present throughout much of the performance (e.g., more difficult rhythms are played at a slower tempo), which detracts from the performance | A consistent underlying pulse is often present throughout much of the performance; however, some phrases may be rushed, which detracts from the performance | A consistent underlying pulse is present throughout most of the performance with minor flaws that do not detract from the performance | A consistent underlying pulse is present throughout the performance | 3 | |
| Intonation | Necessary adjustments are not made to pitches (e.g., alternate fingerings, finger shading, or lipping up or down), which severly detracts from the performance | Some necessary adjustments are not made to pitches (e.g., alternate fingerings, finger shading, or lipping up or down), which may detract from the performance | Many necessary adjustments are made to pitches (e.g., alternate fingerings, finger shading, or lipping up or down), and minor flaws do not detract from the performance | All necessary adjustments are made to pitches (e.g., alternate fingerings, finger shading, or lipping up or down) | | 3.5 | |

| | | | | | | Score |
|---|---|---|---|---|---|---|
| Tone | Uncharacteristic sound that lacks fundamentals (e.g., full breath support, good embouchure, and properly voiced oral cavity) throughout the range and registers of the instrument | Partially characteristic sound that lacks full breath support throughout the range and registers of the instrument | Full characteristic sound that lacks some control in one or more registers of the instrument | Full characteristic sound that is controlled and mature in all registers of the instrument | | 3.5 |
| Articulation | Printed articulations are not performed accurately, and these mistakes detract from many areas of the performance | Printed articulations are performed somewhat accurately, and these mistakes detract from some areas of the performance | Most printed articulations are performed accurately, and mistakes do not severely detract from the performance | All printed articulations performed accurately | | 1.833 |
| Dynamics | Printed dynamics are not performed appropriately, and these mistakes detract from many areas of the performance | Printed dynamics are performed somewhat appropriately, and these mistakes detract from some areas of the performance | Most printed dynamics are performed appropriately, and mistakes do not severely detract from the performance | All printed dynamics are performed appropriately | Dynamics are performed appropriately and go beyond those printed on the page | 1.4 |
| Style (phrasing, agogic weight, and inter-pretation) | Stylistic attributes are not demonstrated | Few stylistic attributes are appropriate for the piece and inconsistently demonstrated throughout the performance | Stylistic attributes are characteristically appropriate for the piece but inconsistently demonstrated throughout the performance | Stylistic attributes are characteristically appropriate for the piece and consistently demonstrated throughout the performance | | 1.834 |
| Marked tempo | Piece performed drastically slower or faster than the MM | Piece performed somewhat slower or faster than the MM | Piece performed close to the MM | Piece performed at the MM | | 1.833 |

## Total Performance Score:

# Appendix D
## Individual Sight-Reading Rubric

**Directions:**

The total score for a criterion is calculated by multiplying the weight for the criterion by the score. The total score for each criterion is summed to produce the total performance score.

## Individual Sight-Reading Rubric

*devised and created by Scott Rush and Dr. Christina Schneider*

| Criteria | Scale | | | | | Weight | Total Score |
|---|---|---|---|---|---|---|---|
| | 1 | 2 | 3 | 4 | 5 | | |
| Pitches | Many pitches performed inaccurately | Some pitches performed accurately, but key signature or accidental mistakes were not corrected | Most pitches performed accurately, and key signature or accidental mistakes were quickly corrected | All pitches performed accurately | | 4.25 | |
| Rhythms | Rhythms performed inaccurately and mistakes detract from many areas of the performance | Some rhythms performed accurately, and duration mistakes detract from the performance | Most rhythms performed accurately, and slight duration mistakes do not detract from the performance | All rhythms performed accurately | | 4.25 | |
| Timing (steady pulse) | A consistent underlying pulse is not present throughout the performance, which severely detracts from the performance | A consistent underlying pulse is not present throughout much of the performance (e.g., more difficult rhythms are played at a slower tempo), which detracts from the performance | A consistent underlying pulse is often present throughout much of the performance; however, some phrases may be rushed, which detracts from the performance | A consistent underlying pulse is present throughout most of the performance with minor flaws that do not detract from the performance | A consistent underlying pulse is present throughout the performance | 3 | |
| Tone | Uncharacteristic sound that lacks fundamentals (e.g., full breath support, good embouchure, and properly voiced oral cavity) throughout the range and registers of the instrument | Partially characteristic sound that lacks full breath support throughout the range and registers of the instrument | Full characteristic sound that lacks some control in one or more registers of the instrument | Full characteristic sound that is controlled and mature in all registers of the instrument | | 4.25 | |

| | | | | |
|---|---|---|---|---|
| Articulation | Printed articulations are not performed accurately, and mistakes detract from many areas of the performance | Some printed articulations are performed accurately, and mistakes detract from some areas of the performance | Most printed articulations are performed accurately, and mistakes do not severely detract from the performance | All printed articulations performed accurately | 4.25 |
| Dynamics | Printed dynamics are not performed and detract from the performance | Printed dynamics are performed somewhat appropriately, and mistakes detract from some areas of the performance | Most printed dynamics are performed appropriately, and mistakes do not severely detract from the performance | All printed dynamics are performed appropriately | All printed dynamics are performed appropriately and go beyond those printed on the page | 3 |
| Marked tempo | Piece performed drastically slower or faster than the MM | Piece performed somewhat slower or faster than the MM | Piece performed close to the MM | Piece performed at the MM | 1 |

## Total Sight-Reading Score:

# Appendix E

## Supplemental Study Guide for
## *Habits of a Successful Band Director*

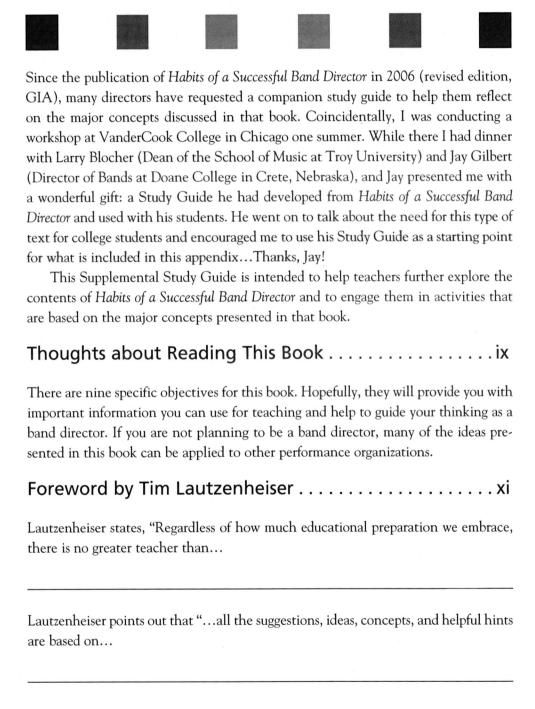

Since the publication of *Habits of a Successful Band Director* in 2006 (revised edition, GIA), many directors have requested a companion study guide to help them reflect on the major concepts discussed in that book. Coincidentally, I was conducting a workshop at VanderCook College in Chicago one summer. While there I had dinner with Larry Blocher (Dean of the School of Music at Troy University) and Jay Gilbert (Director of Bands at Doane College in Crete, Nebraska), and Jay presented me with a wonderful gift: a Study Guide he had developed from *Habits of a Successful Band Director* and used with his students. He went on to talk about the need for this type of text for college students and encouraged me to use his Study Guide as a starting point for what is included in this appendix...Thanks, Jay!

This Supplemental Study Guide is intended to help teachers further explore the contents of *Habits of a Successful Band Director* and to engage them in activities that are based on the major concepts presented in that book.

## Thoughts about Reading This Book . . . . . . . . . . . . . . . . . ix

There are nine specific objectives for this book. Hopefully, they will provide you with important information you can use for teaching and help to guide your thinking as a band director. If you are not planning to be a band director, many of the ideas presented in this book can be applied to other performance organizations.

## Foreword by Tim Lautzenheiser . . . . . . . . . . . . . . . . . . . . xi

Lautzenheiser states, "Regardless of how much educational preparation we embrace, there is no greater teacher than...

_____

Lautzenheiser points out that "...all the suggestions, ideas, concepts, and helpful hints are based on...

_____

What is the rationale Lautzenheiser gives us for embracing *Habits of a Successful Band Director?*

_____

_____

# Chapter One

## Step One: Be Organized and Communicate . . . . . . . . . . 1

–The Life of a Director
–Creating and Communicating Your Philosophy
–Your Professional Mission Statement
–The Handbook
–The Use of the Internet
–The Homework Hotline and the Phone Tree
–The Newsletter
–The Parent Orientation Meeting
–The Chaperone Orientation Meeting

Step one to your success is to be _____

and _____.

Attention and success in these areas should provide you with the opportunity to do what?

_____

_____

Study **Appendix A: The Life of a Band Director Outline** (pp. 127–133). Then make your own outline below by doing the following things:

- Identify the three broad categories (labeled Roman numeral I, II, III).
- Beneath the broad category headings, make a list of the lettered (A, B, C) headings.
- Look at each Arabic number heading (1, 2, 3, etc.) and for each broad category, list these subheadings.

The book is organized with the non-pedagogical director issues presented first. Why?

_____

_____

In the section on **Creating and Communicating Your Philosophy**, an organizational model is provided from which all curricular decisions and program objectives flow. What is the main focus or thrust of this model?

_____

_____

**The Handbook:**

What solutions does a comprehensive handbook provide for your program (page 5)?

_____

_____

Study **Appendix B: The Band Handbook** (page 135). Note the things that are making an impression on you as you read.

_____

_____

One of the greatest favors you can do for parents (and yourself) is to provide a **master schedule** for the entire year. What should be included in the master schedule?

_____

_____

**The Use of the Internet:**

What solutions does using the Internet provide for your program (page 10)?

_____

_____

In addition to the Web, there are three other ways to communicate with parents. What are they?

1. _____

2. _____

3. _____

**The Parent Orientation Meeting:**

"This may sound harsh, but many parents will _____

_____

**The Chaperone Orientation Meeting:**

Chaperone meetings should take place prior to and during trips to train and prepare the chaperones for their responsibilities. There are several issues to discuss. What are they?

_____

_____

_____

## Chapter Two

## Step Two: Work with Parents and Colleagues. . . . . . . 15

–The Role of the Booster Club
–Create a Music-Making Support System through Your Boosters
–Planning a Budget within Your Booster Organization
–Dealing with Difficult Parents
–The Principal/Band Director Relationship
–Taking Care of the Little Things
–Dealing with Other Faculty Members

Dealing with parents and school personnel in an effective manner is key to our success within the band program.

There are several people you will need to inform, collaborate with, and educate. Make a list below of the people you will have to foster relationships with:

_____

_____

In dealing with booster clubs, what are the main points necessary for organizing a thriving support organization?

_____

_____

Name two ways to involve people in the booster organization:

1. _____

2. _____

Most band programs must fundraise to meet the needs of the program. What are some of the pitfalls for raising funds and budgeting with regard to parent groups?

_____

_____

Make a list of all budget items listed on the booster budget (pages 21–23):

_____

_____

_____

_____

_____

**Dealing with Difficult Parents:**

On page 24, several examples of parent problems are cited. What are they?

_____

_____

_____

What is the listed attendance policy (page 24), and why is it effective?

_____

_____

_____

_____

There are two reasons cited to support this rule: Because it's _____

for every student and you can _____it.

Any policy you make will undoubtedly be tested. This is why you should have both

your handbook and your policies reviewed by your building _____

_____

before implementing them.

If you have the unfortunate circumstance of having to deal with a parent who is

truly unreasonable, it is important that you _____, _____

_____, _____.

You must ask yourself this question: "If I had to defend my decisions to the school
board right now, would I have enough documentation to prove my case?" What are
the things you need to document?

_____

_____

_____

If parents wish to discuss issues with you, where should the meeting take place? Why?

_____

_____


## The Principal/Band Director Relationship:

Sometimes, you have to educate your principal, just like you have to educate parents, about the philosophy of the program.

Why is it important to foster a good relationship with the principal at your school?

_____

_____

_____


## Take Care of the "Little Things":

What are the "little things" you will have to address?

_____

_____

When should paperwork for field trips be submitted?

_____

_____

_____

**Dealing with Other Faculty Members:**

Harry Wong states:

_____

_____

Always be willing to do your part and be _____ _____

_____.

Make a list of things you can do to contribute to school life:

_____

_____

_____

_____

# Chapter Three

## Step Three: Manage the Classroom . . . . . . . . . . . . . . . . 31

**The Two First Days of School:**

The "two first days" refers to what?

_____

What do most students and parents *not* do what with regard to the handbook (page 33)?

_____

What must you then do in response?

_____

What are some things that should be done to welcome new students into the band program?

_____

_____

**Rules and Consequences, Expectations, and Procedures:**

A consequence is something that students _____.
Summarize the following…

Expectations:

_____

_____

_____

Procedures:

_____

_____

_____

Rehearsing/Classroom Procedures:

_____

_____

_____

**Discipline versus Punishment:**

Summarize the concept of punishment versus discipline:

_____

_____

_____

**The Rehearsal Set-up and Schedule:**

What are the pitfalls of an unplanned rehearsal?

_____

_____

_____

_____

What things can be done to ensure a successful rehearsal?

_____

_____

_____

_____

# Chapter Four

## Step Four: Understand the Importance of the Warm-up . . 41

-Purpose of the Warm-up
-The Full Band Warm-up
-Breathing Exercises as Part of the Warm-up Process
-What About the Percussionists?

**Purpose of the Warm-up:**

What is the importance of warming up?

_____

_____

The warm-up should begin…

_____

_____

What are the two primary purposes of the warm-up?

1. _____

2. _____

**The Full Band Warm-up:**

What are the bases for full band warm-ups?

_____

_____

Each develops different skills. What are they?

_____

_____

**Breathing Exercises as Part of the Warm-up Process:**

The purpose of breathing exercises is twofold:

1. _____

2. _____

Name three variations on the amount of air needed to play (page 48):

1. _____

2. _____

3. _____

Explain the following diagram (page 49):

$$T + OH = TOH$$

_____

_____

_____

_____

**What About the Percussionists?**

What about the percussionists? Name the key points in this section:

_____

_____

_____

_____

_____

_____

# Chapter Five

## Step Five: Incorporate Effective Rehearsal Strategies . .53

–Probing Questions
–Attacks
–Timing
–Tuning
–Balance
–Blend
–B–M–E of Notes
–Playing "In Tone"
–Five-Step Articulation Exercise
–Components of Playing

Write the quote below the chapter heading:

_____

_____

Much of what we teach involves some type of _____.

If you are prepared to teach _____ _____,

the end product should be _____ _____.

One of the most important concepts we teach is _____.

Provide examples to teach the aforementioned skill.

_____

**Probing Questions:**

Define the concept of probing questions:

_____

_____

What disturbing results did Dr. Blocher's study bring to light?

_____

_____

For the following headings, note characteristics you have observed that would define the component as being poorly performed...

Attacks:

_____

_____

Timing:

_____

_____

Tuning:

_____

_____

Balance:

_____

_____

Blend:

_____

_____

B–M–E:

_____

_____

B–M–E refers to the what?

_____

If a note is followed by a rest, you release the note on the _____.

On page 59, the **five-step articulation process** is presented. I will describe the first example:

1. Slur two-tongue two _____

Describe the remaining examples:

2. _____

3. _____

4. _____

5. _____

**Components of Playing:**

The Components of Playing is about a story involving Daniel Katzen, a horn player in the BSO. In the story, Katzen took out a piece of paper and numbered it from 1 to 25. He then filled in the 1st component and the 25th component.

The Components of Playing is nothing more than a list of:

_____

_____

Practice doesn't make perfect, only...

_____

_____

Directors would really be missing the point if they did not realize that classroom

management, rehearsal set-up and pacing, and teaching strategies _____

_____  _____  _____.

## Chapter Six

## Step Six: Make High-Quality Literature Your Curriculum . . 63

-Wind Literature
-Large Ensemble Programming
-Chamber Music
-Woodwind Quintet Literature
-Brass Quintet Literature
-Small Ensemble Literature
-Percussion Ensemble Literature

Many successful band directors make a fundamental mistake their first year of teaching. What is it?

_____

_____

The reality is that there are great pieces of music regardless of the grade level of music, and…

_____

_____

What are the programming pitfalls?

_____

_____

_____

_____

What are the fundamental books (page 64)?

_____

_____

_____

_____

**Wind Literature:**

List the wind literature resources:

_____

_____

_____

_____

_____

_____

_____

**Large Ensemble Programming:**

What did Harry Begian say about programming?

_____

_____

**Chamber Music:**

What is the best way for your students to improve?

_____

_____

What is the second best way?

_____

_____

Why?

_____

_____

A list of chamber literature is presented in *Habits*. Below each ensemble, list works of interest you could use in your program.

**Woodwind quintet literature:**

_____

_____

**Brass quintet literature:**

_____

_____

**Small ensemble literature:**

_____

_____

**Percussion ensemble literature:**

_____

_____

## Chapter Seven

# Step Seven: Assess for Success . . . . . . . . . . . . . . . . . . . .75

**Assessment:**

List the pitfalls of poor assessment:

_____

_____

_____

_____

**Model One—The Four T's:**

For each of **The Four T's** make notes on ideas, helpful hints, or suggestions for teaching the concept:

Playing **"in time"**:

_____

_____

_____

_____

_____

_____

Playing "**in tune**":

_____

_____

_____

_____

_____

Playing "**in tone**":

_____

_____

_____

_____

Playing "**with technique**":

_____

_____

_____

_____

## Sequencing Units of Study:

From the notes you have taken on The Four T's, write ten concepts and skills to be taught and how you might assess them:

| Musical Concept | Skill to Be Taught | Assessment Tool |
|---|---|---|
|  |  |  |
|  |  |  |
|  |  |  |
|  |  |  |
|  |  |  |
|  |  |  |
|  |  |  |
|  |  |  |
|  |  |  |
|  |  |  |

**Model Two—Teaching to the Correct Level of Difficulty:**

When determining the correct level of difficulty, you were asked to consider a specific question. What is it?

_____

_____

_____

What are the names of the three levels of mastery within the **three-tiered assessment model**?

1. _____

2. _____

3. _____

Describe how the three-tiered assessment model works:

_____

_____

_____

_____

_____

Summarize the positive aspects of the three following ideas...

Assessing recorded examples:

_____

_____

_____

_____

Using the National Standards:

_____

_____

_____

_____

What to teach and assess:

_____

_____

_____

_____

## Chapter Eight

–The Difference Between Power and Ownership
–How to Begin the Selection Process
–The Leadership Mission Statement
–Team Building
–Taking Care of the Customers

What are the pitfalls of student leadership?

_____

_____

_____

_____

Teachers and student leaders share:

☐ the same qualities  ☐ similar qualities

☐ little in common  ☐ nothing in common

List the solutions offered on page 102 here:

_____

_____

_____

_____

**The Difference Between Power and Ownership:**

What is the difference between power and ownership?

_____

_____

**How to Begin the Selection Process:**

Summarize the major points of selecting high-quality student leaders:

_____

_____

_____

_____

_____

**Team Building:**

What are the techniques presented for team building?

_____

_____

_____

_____

What are the tips presented for goal setting?

_____

_____

_____

**Taking Care of the Customers:**

Which students are highlighted as "valued customers" if you want your program to survive?

_____

_____

Summarize the 10 points in the section on **Taking Care of the Customers:**

1. _____

2. _____

3. _____

4. _____

5. _____

6. _____

7. _____

8. _____

9. _____

10. _____

Answer the five questions about leadership from the **Chapter Checklist**...

How do you choose student leaders?

_____

_____

What criteria are you going to use to select leaders?

_____

_____

How do you train them once they are selected?

_____

_____

How would you characterize your style of leadership?

_____

_____

Are you a servant leader?

_____

_____

# Chapter Nine

## Step Nine: Beg, Borrow, Steal, and Hone Your Skills . . . .109

–The Effective Director
–The Effectiveness Checklist
–Incorporating the Ideas of Others
–The Symphonic Camp
–The Collage Concert
–Joint Concerts
–Masterclasses
–Conferences
–The Conducting Workshop
–The Mentor Teacher
–Private Lessons

**The Effective Director:**

A colleague teaching in the Washington DC area offered what advice to future teachers?

_____

_____

Name the four solutions from page 110 here:

1. _____

2. _____

3. _____

4. _____

**The Effectiveness Checklist:**

Look at the effectiveness checklist. **Do not rate yourself for this exercise.** Rather, reflect on the questions from the list and note areas that need improvement:

_____

_____

_____

_____

_____

Make brief notes on how you may incorporate each of the following activities/events into your program…

The Symphonic Camp:

_____

_____

The Collage Concert:

_____

_____

Joint Concerts:

_____

_____

Masterclasses:

_____

_____

Conferences:

_____

_____

The Conducting Workshop:

_____

_____

Private Lessons:

_____

_____

# Chapter Ten

    –Make Music
    –Will my present mood allow us to make music?
    –Are students becoming technicians or musicians?
    –A Final Note—Keep It in Perspective and Take Care of Yourself

**Make Music:**

The title of *Habits* could be _____ _____ _____

_____ _____ \_\_\_\_\_ _____.

This text has set out to dispel the myth that you have to be a natural-born teacher. What, then, has been the two main points of *Habits* thus far?

1._____

2._____

All of that said, the end goal is _____ _____.

What is the overwhelming sentiment to "Why do we do this"?

_____

_____

Music at the middle school or high school level is something that should be experienced. By whom?

_____

_____

What was the point of the Moscow Conservatory student's comment on the American orchestra concert?

_____

_____

**A Final Note – Keep It in Perspective and Take Care of Yourself:**

What is one of the goals of *Habits*?

_____

_____

Sometimes good teachers have trouble doing what?

_____

_____

Keeping everything in perspective can be a challenge. Fill in the following:

| Item | Rating | Goal | Date |
|------|--------|------|------|
| Spiritual life | | | |
| Relationships in your life | | | |
| Physical health | | | |
| Mental health | | | |
| Self-help and personal growth | | | |

Write the Paul Yoder quote here:

_____

_____

_____

_____

# The Final Checklist

## *Habits of a Successful Band Director*
## Scott Rush

This checklist is included for your reference when you finally get your first job (or if you've been teaching for ten, twenty, or thirty years and still want to improve). Your attention to these details and preparation will be an essential step in helping you to become a successful teacher.

**Chapter One Checklist:**

**Be organized and communicate.** Take a mental inventory of your organizational plan, and rate yourself in the following areas:

1. A professional mission statement
2. The band handbook
3. The band newsletter or Web site
4. A master schedule for the year
5. The parent and chaperone orientation meeting

**Chapter Two Checklist:**

1. Are you able to effectively communicate your philosophy about the program?
2. Are your policies consistent and enforceable?
3. Do you have the believability as a band director to encourage all parents to be involved in the total program?
4. Do you have a system for involving parents?
5. What would your professional colleagues say about you?

**Chapter Three Checklist:**

Apply the following questions to your particular teaching situation:
1. Do you have a procedure for the first few days of school?
2. Can you clearly articulate your policies, procedures, and expectations?
3. Do your rehearsals run smoothly?
4. Do you find yourself walking to the podium without a plan?
5. Do your students finish rehearsals with a sense of accomplishment?

## Chapter Four Checklist:

Evaluate your warm-up routine in the following areas:
1. Does your warm-up routine get the chops (or their equivalents) in playing condition?
2. Does your warm-up routine build stamina and strength?
3. Does your routine cover musical concepts that will carry over into the rehearsal?
4. Does your routine teach components of ensemble performance?
5. Do you use breathing exercises to maximize lung capacity and aid in tonal development?

## Chapter Five Checklist:

1. Do you have a strategy for teaching musical concepts?
2. Do you have a system for teaching your students how to practice?
3. Do you have a system for teaching your students what to practice?
4. Is your classroom dialogue filled with solutions to musical problems?
5. Do your students feel they are actively involved in coming up with solutions to troubleshoot various musical problems?

## Chapter Six Checklist:

Answer the following questions in regard to literature:
1. Do you use method/supplemental books on a daily basis?
2. What are your criteria for determining the musical worth of a composition?
3. Are your choices for literature a good match for your ensemble?
4. Is chamber music an integral part of your band program?
5. Do you provide a comprehensive percussion class/ensemble for your students?

## Chapter Seven Checklist:

Rate your effectiveness in teaching the following concepts:
1. Timing
2. Tuning
3. Tone
4. Technique
5. Assessing the correct level of difficulty for your students

**Chapter Eight Checklist:**

Answer the following questions about leadership:
1. How do you choose student leaders?
2. What criteria are used to select leaders?
3. How do you train them once they are selected?
4. How would you characterize your style of leadership?
5. What message are you instilling in student leaders to prepare them to interact with other students? Is it one of giving and taking?

**Chapter Nine Checklist:**

Every band program is different. Some ideas work well in certain situations, while others do not. List five ideas of others you would like to incorporate into your program:

1. _____

2. _____

3. _____

4. _____

5. _____

**Chapter Ten Checklist:**

- Spiritual life
- Relationships in your life
- Physical health
- Mental health
- Self-help and personal growth

# References

Battisti, Frank. *On Becoming a Conductor*. Galesville: Meredith Music, 2007.

Bennis, Warren. *On Becoming a Leader*. New York: Basic Book, 1989 (first edition), 2003 (second edition).

Blocher, Larry, et al. *Teaching Music Through Performance in Band, Volume 3*. Chicago: GIA Publications, 2000.

Gardner, John W. *Self-Renewal: The Individual and the Innovative Society*. New York: W. W. Norton and Company, 1996.

Jenson, Eric. *Arts with the Brain in Mind*. Alexandria: Association for Supervision and Curriculum Development, 2001.

Lang, Scott. *Leadership Travel Guide*. Chicago: GIA Publications, 2007.

McBeth, W. Francis. *Effective Performance of Band Music*. San Antonio: Southern Music Company, 1972.

Pausch, Randy, and Jeffrey Zaslow. *The Last Lecture*. New York: Hyperion, 2008.

Walter, Bruno. *Of Music and Music Making*. New York: W. W. Norton and Company, 1957.

Zander, Rosamund, and Benjamin Zander. *The Art of Possibility*. New York: Penguin Group, 2000.

# About the Author

Scott Rush is Director of Bands at Wando High School in Mount Pleasant, South Carolina. He is a graduate of the New England Conservatory of Music in Boston, Massachusetts, where he received his Master of Music in French Horn Performance and studied with Boston Symphony principal hornist Charles Kavalovski. While at NEC, Mr. Rush studied conducting under Frank Battisti and Pascal Verrot, and he was a member of the NEC Symphony under the baton of Carl St. Claire. He was a Concerto Competition winner and member of the Boston Philharmonic under Benjamin Zander. Mr. Rush received his Bachelor's degree from the University of South Carolina, where he studied under Robert Pruzin and was the recipient of the Arthur Fraser Award for Outstanding Graduating Senior in Music.

In his seventeenth year of teaching (and ninth at Wando High School), Mr. Rush's bands have received consistent Superior ratings in the areas of concert and marching band. The Wando Symphonic Band performed at the 2007 Midwest International Band and Orchestra Clinic in Chicago, Illinois. His bands have also been named National Honor Group for the National Adjudicators Invitational in Chattanooga and South Carolina State 5A Marching Band Champions on three occasions. The Wando Symphonic Band performed at the 2002 Bands of America National Concert Band Festival, 2002 SCMEA Convention, 2003 Southern Division MENC Conference, 2004 University of South Carolina Band Clinic, and 2006 National Concert Band and Orchestra Invitational through the Disney Honors program. In 2008, the Wando Band program received the prestigious Sudler Flag of Honor from the John Philip Sousa Foundation.

Mr. Rush is active as clinician and adjudicator, having presented workshops and clinics for various universities, school districts, and conferences throughout the United States. He is author of the highly touted book, *Habits of a Successful Band Director* (GIA), and *Curriculum Guide for Instrumental Music* for the South Carolina State Department of Education. He has been the recipient of the National Band Association's Citation of Excellence on four occasions and was named Teacher of the Year for 2004. He also received the 2007 Outstanding Bandmaster Award from the Theta Chapter of Phi Beta Mu. Mr. Rush is nationally board certified by NBPTS. He has been active as a professional hornist since 1985. He serves on the board of the National Band Association, South Carolina Band Directors Association, and South Carolina Music Educators Association. Professional affiliations include National Band Association, Phi Beta Mu, and Phi Mu Alpha.

His wife Michelle teaches general music at Pinckney Elementary in Mount Pleasant, South Carolina, where they enjoy the company of their son, Thomas.